# Key Stage 3 Science
# National Strategy Workbooks

These books have been <u>written specifically</u> to
cover the Scheme of Work.  That means they also cover
the Yearly Teaching Objectives.

Each unit in the book covers one unit from the Scheme of Work.
And there's even the odd ever-so-nearly entertaining bit,
just to help keep you awake.

# What CGP is all about

Our sole aim here at CGP is to produce the highest quality
books — carefully written, immaculately presented
and dangerously close to being funny.

Then we work our socks off to get them out to you
— at the cheapest possible prices.

# Contents

## Unit 8A — Food and Digestion

Food is Important ..............................................................1
Types of Food ..................................................................2
Food is Useful ..................................................................3
A Balanced Diet ................................................................4
The Digestive System ........................................................6
Digestive Enzymes ............................................................8
Products of Digestion ........................................................9

## Unit 8B — Respiration

Digestion and Respiration ................................................10
Products of Respiration ....................................................11
Transport of Substances for Respiration ............................12
The Heart and Circulation ................................................13
Respiration and Exercise ..................................................14
Role of the Lungs in Respiration ......................................15
Respiration in other Living Organisms ..............................16

## Unit 8C — Microbes and Disease

Micro-Organisms ..............................................................17
Investigating Yeast ..........................................................18
Growing Micro-organisms ................................................19
Micro-organisms can Cause Disease ..................................20
Preventing the Spread of Disease ......................................21
Natural Barriers ..............................................................22
Medicines ........................................................................23
Immunisation ..................................................................24

## Unit 8D — Ecological Relationships

Classification ..................................................................25
Habitat Data Collection ....................................................26
Communities and Organisms ............................................27
Environmental Conditions ................................................28
Population Size ................................................................29
Feeding Relationships ......................................................30

## Unit 8E — Atoms and Elements

Materials and Elements ....................................................31
Element Structure ............................................................32
Types of Element ............................................................33
Compounds and Molecules ..............................................35
Simple Chemical Reactions ..............................................37
Element or Not? ..............................................................38

## Unit 8F — Compounds and Mixtures

Compounds and Formulas ................................................39
Compounds and their Components ....................................40
Do Compounds React Chemically? ..................................41
Mixtures ..........................................................................42
Melting and Boiling Points ..............................................43
Elements, Compounds and Mixtures..................................44

# Contents

## Unit 8G — Rocks and Weathering

Rock Properties ............................................................... 45
Biological and Chemical Weathering ...................... 46
Physical Weathering ........................................................ 47
Effects of Weathering: Sediment ........................... 48
Sediment Layers .............................................................. 50

## Unit 8H — The Rock Cycle

Sedimentary Rock ............................................................ 52
Sedimentary Rock: Limestone ................................. 53
Metamorphic Rock ........................................................... 54
Igneous Rock ..................................................................... 55
Types of Igneous Rock .................................................. 56
The Rock Cycle ................................................................. 57

## Unit 8I — Heating and Cooling

Temperature ........................................................................ 58
Conduction ........................................................................... 60
Expansion ............................................................................. 62
Convection ............................................................................ 63
Radiation ............................................................................... 64
Reducing Heat Loss ........................................................ 65
Changing State .................................................................. 66
Heating and Cooling — Review .............................. 67

## Unit 8J — Magnets and Electromagnets

Magnets ................................................................................. 68
Magnetic Fields ................................................................ 70
Electromagnets ................................................................ 72

## Unit 8K — Light

How Light Travels ........................................................... 73
When Light Meets an Object ..................................... 74
How Mirrors Work ........................................................... 75
The Spectrum and Bending Light ........................... 76
Colours ................................................................................... 77

## Unit 8L — Sound

Pitch and Loudness ......................................................... 78
Sound Waves ....................................................................... 79
The Speed of Sound ....................................................... 80
Hearing ................................................................................... 81
Investigating Sound ...................................................... 83

The Answers ....................................................................... 85

Published by Coordination Group Publications Ltd.


*Contributors:*
Paddy Gannon
Barbara Green
Gemma Hallam
Keith Hudson
Sarah Irving
Steve Parkinson
Barry Pywell


*Design and Graphics by:*
Chris Dennett
Dominic Hall
Simon Little
Becky May
Joanne Morgan
Alison Palin
Katherine Reed
Julie Schofield
James Paul Wallis
Chrissy Williams


*With Thanks to:*
David Worthington and
Eileen Worthington for the proofreading.

ISBN: 978 1 84146 245 5

Groovy website: www.cgpbooks.co.uk

Printed by Elanders Hindson Ltd, Newcastle upon Tyne.

# Food is Important

**Q1** The words in the table below are mixed up. Write a sentence about each organism, linking it to its correct source of food.

E.g. *a cow eats grass.*

| Organism | Food source |
|----------|-------------|
| Cow | Flies |
| Snail | Makes its own food |
| Spider | Meat and vegetables |
| Green plant | Grass |
| Human | Algae |

**Q2** Food is a source of energy. Which of these activities requires the most energy?

playing tennis   doing your homework

sleeping    walking to school

**Q3** Why is it important for you to eat a good breakfast?

**Q4** Rearrange these letters to make a new word. (Clue: the word is something that we need food for.)

**worght**

**Q5** Movement and growth both need a lot of energy, but there is another process that needs energy, which goes on in everyone. Without it we would wear away. What is it?

**Q6** **Write** out the **true statements only** from the following list:

Animals and plants can make their own food.

Old people are not very active so they do not need food.

Food provides the energy needed for movement.

All living organisms need energy.

Food is the raw material for growth and repair.

A diet of chips, sweets and fizzy drinks is good for you.

# *Types of Food*

Q1   Copy out the diagram and use the clues to find the words.

**Down**
1.   Found in lean meat.
2.   Butter, lard and suet are forms of this.
4.   Examples: calcium, iron and sodium.

**Across**
2.   Bran is a good source of this.
3.   Starch and sugar
5.   Found in fresh fruit and vegetables.
6.   94% of a cabbage is this.

Q2   Use the information in the table to answer these questions about Chruncho breakfast cereal:

a) What food substance is there most of?

b) Is there more fat or protein?

c) How many grams of fibre are there in every 100g of Chruncho?

d) Name the minerals in Chruncho.

e) How many different vitamins are present?

| Nutritional content per 100g | |
|---|---|
| Protein | 8.0g |
| Carbohydrate | 71.0g |
| Fat | 4.0g |
| Fibre | 9.0g |
| Sodium | 0.6g |
| Iron | 8.8mg |
| Vitamins: | |
| Thiamin | 0.9mg |
| Riboflavin | 1.0mg |
| Niacin | 11.3mg |

Q3   Samantha adds a few drops of dilute iodine solution to a piece of bread.

a)   What colour is iodine solution?

b)   What colour will the bread turn?

c)   This will show the presence of which food substance?

Q4   Jumbo Wilson is testing a sample of a sports drink to see if it contains glucose. He adds Benedict's reagent then heats the sample in a beaker of hot water.

a)   The sample changes to a brick red colour.  Is glucose present?

b)   What safety equipment should Jumbo wear when carrying out this test?

Q5   Describe how you would use alcohol and cold water to test for fat.

Q6   Construct a **Venn diagram** showing the combinations of carbohydrate, protein and fat in the following foods:

rice, bacon, peanuts, cream, white fish, egg, beans, steak, pasta, chips, oily fish, melon

# _Food is Useful_

**Q1**  Copy and complete these sentences using the words from the box.

| bread   oranges   fish   milk   fat   fibre |

Maaaa! the man's still a'wrigglin in ma bread.

a)  ................. is a good source of carbohydrate.

b)  Good sources of protein are ................. and meat.

c)  Margarine is a good source of ................. .

d)  Celery and wholemeal bread contain ................. .

e)  ................. contain a lot of vitamin C.

f)  ................. is a good source of calcium.

**Q2**  The table below contains nutritional information about different foods.

| Food | Percentage mass (%) | | | | | |
|---|---|---|---|---|---|---|
|  | Protein | Fat | Carbohydrate | Water | Fibre | Vitamins & minerals |
| Fresh fish | 18 | 3 | 0 | 77 | 0 | 2 |
| Dried fish | 63 | 10 | 0 | 18 | 0 | 9 |
| Meat | 18 | 18 | 0 | 63 | 0 | 1 |
| Eggs | 12 | 10 | 0 | 78 | 0 | <1 |
| Cow's milk | 4 | 4 | 5 | 87 | 0 | <1 |
| Soya beans | 34 | 18 | 34 | 9 | 5 | <1 |
| Broad beans | 20 | 1 | 60 | 12 | 7 | <1 |
| Cabbage | 0 | 1 | 4 | 94 | 1 | <1 |

Use information from the table to draw:

a)  a pie chart showing the relative amount of each nutrient present in cow's milk.

b)  a bar chart showing the percentage of protein in each food.

c)  a bar chart showing the percentage of each nutrient present in soya beans and broad beans.

**Q3**  Write five sentences using a word from the left-hand column and the correct phrase from the right-hand column.

| Fat | in small quantities are necessary for good health |
|---|---|
| Carbohydrate | prevents constipation |
| Protein | provides energy |
| Fibre | is used for growth and repair |
| Vitamins and minerals | provides energy |

**Q4**  Explain why:

a)  a child suffering from a shortage of protein does not grow as fast as he/she should.

b)  body builders eat eggs rather than bread.

c)  marathon runners often eat rice and pasta before a race.

# A Balanced Diet

**Q1**  Copy and complete the sentences below by guessing the missing words.

A b _ _ _ _ _ _ _ diet contains c _ _ _ _ _ _ _ _ _ _, fat, proteins,

v _ _ _ _ _ _ _, minerals, f _ _ _ _ and w _ _ _ _ in the correct amounts.

*Each dash is a letter.*

**Q2**  Copy out these statements, putting them into three lists under the headings, **True**, **False**, **Possibly true**:

- Eating too much carbohydrate can make you fat.

- "Organic" foods are produced without manufactured fertilisers, pesticides or weedkillers.

- "Organic" foods are better for you than ordinary foods.

- Green vegetables are good for you.

- Eating crusts makes your hair curly.

- Pregnant women need more minerals in their diet.

- Eating vegetable oils rather than animal fats will reduce the chance of heart disease.

- The more vitamins you eat, the healthier you will be.

- Cancer of the bowel is caused by not eating enough fibre.

- Eating fruit and vegetables can help prevent constipation.

- Many years ago sailors on long sea journeys ate limes to prevent a disease called scurvy.

**Q3**  Jumbo is looking at information about dietary supplements from two different manufacturers.  He thinks one set of information is reliable and the other is unreliable.  The information has been mixed up.  Write down the pieces of information that would show him a source is reliable.

- The product was tested on rats.

- He found articles on the Internet that described benefits of taking the product.

- Many human volunteers took the supplement and were examined by doctors every month for two years.

- The health of the volunteers was compared with a matched group of people who didn't take the supplement.

- The product can only be purchased by mail order.

- The original research work on the supplement was published in a well known scientific journal.

No, no, no... Giant's flesh won't give you the vitamins you need.

# A Balanced Diet

Q1    Rewrite this quiz sheet matching each question to the correct answer.

| QUESTIONS | ANSWERS |
|---|---|
| ✶ Why do we need food? | Fibre. |
| ✶ Give three uses of energy in the body. | Beans. |
| ✶ In the biuret test, what colour shows that protein is present? | Carbohydrates and fat. |
| ✶ When testing for sugar what must you do after adding Benedict's reagent? | Vitamins and minerals. |
| ✶ Name the reagent used to test for starch. | Iron. |
| ✶ What does a balanced diet contain? | Iodine solution. |
| ✶ Give three good sources of protein. | Carbohydrate, protein and fat. |
| ✶ Bread and rice are good sources of this. | Heat it. |
| ✶ Small amounts of these are present in foods. | Growth and repair. |
| ✶ Nuts are a good source of which nutrients? | Water. |
| ✶ Liver is a good source of which mineral? | Growth, repair and movement. |
| ✶ For which two processes is protein needed? | Carbohydrate. |
| ✶ Which two nutrients provide energy? | The right amount of each nutrient. |
| ✶ Which provides more energy per gram, carbohydrate or fat? | Sodium. |
| ✶ These are a good source of protein for vegetarians. | To provide raw materials and for energy. |
| ✶ Herbivores can digest this but we can't. | Meat, fish and beans. |
| ✶ Humans can only live a few days without this. | Fat. |
| ✶ Processed foods often contain too much of this mineral. | Violet or blue. |

Q2    A newspaper prints an article about a woman called Tinkabell Hoofnobble who claims to live on nothing but chocolate.  She says that she feels great and therefore it proves that you do not need a balanced diet to be healthy.  Give two reasons why you would not consider this to be good evidence.

## A quiz — wow. Can Science really be this much fun...

So you want to be constipated, malnourished with no teeth and furry, clogged-up arteries?  No? Well you'd better get a proper balanced diet then.  Learn about the seven food types — carbohydrate, fat, protein, fibre, water, vitamins and minerals — what each one is for and how much you need of it.

# The Digestive System

Q1 The diagram below shows Horace's digestive system. Copy out the diagram and complete the labels by choosing the correct word from the box.

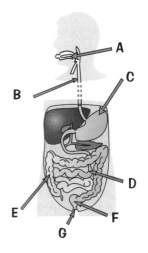

| rectum | gullet | anus |
| small intestine | | stomach |
| mouth | | large intestine |

Q2 Bruce is exploring what happens to food in the gut. He uses visking tubing to make a model of the small intestine. Visking tubing lets small molecules pass through, but not large ones. He fills the bag with starch suspension, washes it and puts it into a beaker of water.

Starch suspension in a visking tubing bag

Pure water

The next day they tested samples of water from the beaker for starch.
All the results were negative.

a) What does this experiment tell you about the size of starch molecules?

b) What will have to happen to the starch molecules before they can get through the tubing?

Q3 The diagram represents a molecule of protein. (Good, isn't it?)

Draw the molecule to show how much would be broken down in:

a) the mouth

b) the stomach

c) the small intestine

*Don't worry about the different shapes — just draw diagrams to represent the level to which protein is broken down at each stage.*

Don't eat your own belly...
... it's stupid and messy.

# The Digestive System

Q1 A student set up an experiment to find out what happens to starch in the digestive system. She poured starch suspension into visking tubing bag A and then did the same with bag B but this time she added a small amount of enzyme solution. She washed both bags under the tap then placed each bag in a separate beaker of water. Every minute she took a sample of water from each beaker and tested them for the presence of glucose.

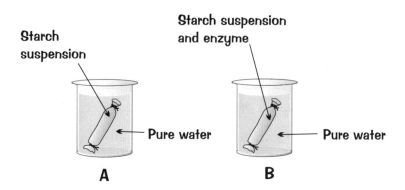

Starch suspension
Starch suspension and enzyme
Pure water
Pure water
A
B

**Results:**

| Time (min) | Amount of glucose present | |
|---|---|---|
| | A | B |
| 0 (start) | None | None |
| 1 | None | None |
| 2 | None | None |
| 3 | None | A little |
| 4 | None | A lot |
| 5 | None | A lot |

a) The student used Benedict's reagent. How could she tell when there was glucose in some of the samples?

b) Did either of the water samples taken at the start of the experiment contain glucose?

c) Where had the glucose come from?

d) Starch molecules are large and insoluble. Glucose molecules are small and soluble. Suggest what the enzyme may have done to the starch molecules.

e) In this model, which part of the digestive system is represented by the visking tubing?

f) What does the water represent?

## The Digestive System — it all begins in the McVitie's factory...

Poor old Horace up there with all his <u>inner bits</u> on show and an arrow pointing at his anus. It's not very dignified, is it... Anyway, here's the gist of these pages: the food we eat contains <u>large</u> molecules like starch and proteins. The digestive system <u>breaks them down</u> into small ones that can be absorbed into the blood.

# *Digestive Enzymes*

**Q1**   Copy and complete this sentence using the words below.

| enzymes   absorbed   digested   smaller |

Food is .................. by .................. in the gut to form ..................
molecules which can be .................. into the blood.

**Q2**   Conditions vary in different parts of the gut.

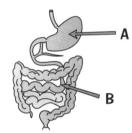

a)   Name organs A and B.

b)   In which of these organs are conditions acidic?

c)   In which organ are conditions alkaline?

**Q3**   Humans maintain a constant body temperature.  Which of these is normal body temperature?

27 °C     35 °C     37 °C     45 °C     47 °C

**Q4**   A scientist isolated a protein-digesting enzyme from the stomach and another from the small intestine.  He used them in this investigation.

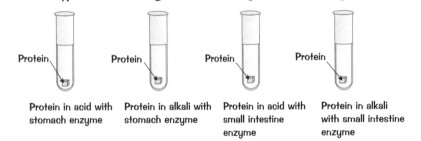

**Results**:

After two hours, the cubes of protein could not be seen in Tubes A and D but were still visible in B and C.

a) i)  Which condition is necessary for the stomach enzyme to work?
   ii) Which condition is necessary for the small intestine enzyme to work?

b) Why did the temperature, the size of the protein and the amount of enzyme have to be the same for each tube?

c) Suggest why the scientist chose to carry out all of his experiments at 37 °C rather than 23 °C (room temperature).

d) What piece of equipment could he use to keep the tubes at a constant temperature?

# Products of Digestion

Q1   Which substance carries glucose from the small intestine to all the cells of the body?

Q2   The molecules that make up plant fibre are large and insoluble. Humans do not make the enzyme that can digest fibre molecules. What happens to the fibre in our food?

Q3   Cows, sheep and other herbivores do have the fibre-digesting enzyme in their guts. What will happen to the fibre in their diet?

Q4   Copy and complete the diagram below using the words in the box.

| Growth | Digested |
| Egested | Transported in blood |
| Not digested | Repair | Energy |

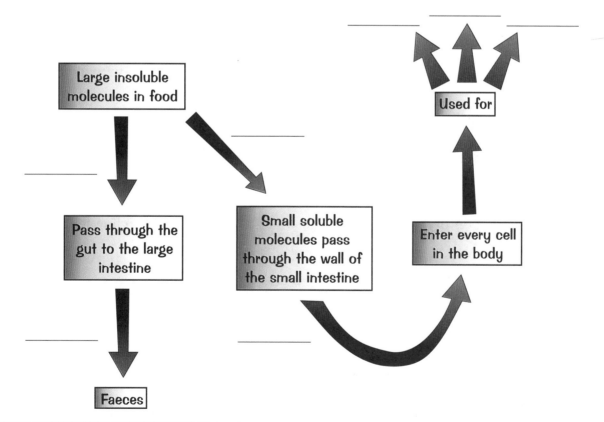

Large insoluble molecules in food

Pass through the gut to the large intestine

Faeces

Small soluble molecules pass through the wall of the small intestine

Enter every cell in the body

Used for

## *Yeah man, I really dig egestion — Rock on...*

So remember, it's <u>enzymes</u> which break down the big food molecules so that they can pass through the small intestine into the blood. And these enzymes work best at certain <u>temperatures</u> and <u>pH levels</u>. OK that's it, lesson over.                    (You can go home now...)

## **Digestion and Respiration**

**Q1**  Write down three reasons why the human body needs food.  Choose from options A-E.

> A)    for growth
>
> B)    to keep clean
>
> C)    for the production of body heat
>
> D)    for photosynthesis
>
> E)    for the synthesis of new materials

**Q2**  True or false?  *"The products of digestion are transported around the body in the blood."*

**Q3**  Copy these sentences and fill in the blanks using the words in the box.

| blood | energy | high-energy drinks | muscle cells | glucose |
|-------|--------|--------------------|--------------|---------|

a) Carbohydrates are broken down by digestion into small ................... molecules.

b) Glucose is a source of ................... .  There is a lot of glucose in ................... .

c) Glucose molecules are transported in the ................... to cells, e.g. ................... .

**Q4**  Circle the things that are needed for aerobic respiration.

oxygen        carbon dioxide        roughage        glucose        nitrogen        fatty acids

**Q5**  Read the description of the experiment.  Answer the questions by circling the right words.

2.5 cm³ of icing sugar was put in a tin can.  A lid was put on the tin, leaving a small gap.
A lighted candle was put through the gap to set the icing sugar on fire.
The sugar ignited and the explosion blew the lid off the tin.

a) The people doing this experiment should have been wearing [safety glasses / rubber gloves].

b) The reaction in the tin was between sugar and [oxygen / carbon dioxide].

c) In aerobic respiration a reaction takes place between oxygen and [amylase / glucose].

d) Respiration takes place in [transit / cells].

e) Respiration is a much more [controlled / explosive] reaction than the one in the tin experiment.

# Products of Respiration

Q1   The diagram shows an experiment to test if heat energy is produced in respiration.
Answer the questions below.

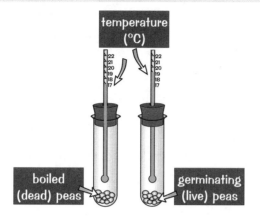

a)  What is the temperature of the boiled (dead) peas?

b)  What is the temperature of the germinating (live) peas?

c)  What are the germinating peas producing?

Q2   Energy is one product of respiration.  Name the other two.

Q3   The diagram shows an experiment to find out if carbon dioxide is a product of respiration.
Answer the questions below.

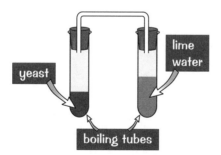

a)  In the experiment the lime water turned a cloudy, milky colour.  What caused this?

b)  If the experiment was done with dead yeast would the lime water turn cloudy?

Q4   Complete the word equation for respiration.

glucose   +   _____   ➔   carbon dioxide   +   _____   +   energy

---

## Want to test if heat energy is produced? — yes peas...

Respiration (not breathing) is what the oxygen you breathe in is used for — to make energy.
The reaction is a bit like when you burn a fuel — you get $CO_2$, $H_2O$ and energy out at the end.
Just don't go thinking that cells burn the glucose.  (Now that does sound nasty...)

# Transport of Substances for Respiration

Q1    Copy these sentences and fill in the blanks using the words in the box.

| oxygen    water    bloodstream    glucose    cells    transported |

Carbohydrates are broken down into ................. in the stomach.  This is transported around

the body in the ................. .  Glucose molecules pass from the bloodstream into

................. .  ................. is breathed into the lungs and then passes into the bloodstream.

It is ................. by the bloodstream to the cells.  The waste products of respiration, carbon

dioxide and ................. , are transferred out of the cells into the bloodstream.


Q2    The diagram shows the human body.  Follow the instructions below.

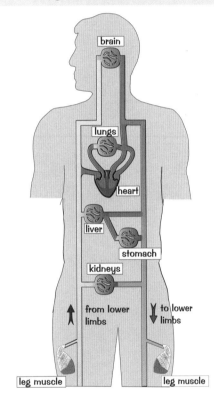

a) Draw onto the diagram the path of a glucose molecule
   from the stomach to a leg muscle cell.

b) Use a different colour to draw the path of an oxygen
   molecule from the lungs to a leg muscle cell.


Q3    Tick whether the following sentences are true or false.

                                                                    TRUE    FALSE

a)  Substances are exchanged between the blood and nearby cells.      ☐        ☐

b)  The substances exchanged include phloem and xylem.               ☐        ☐

c)  The exchange of substances happens next to the blood capillaries.  ☐        ☐

d)  Substances are only transferred into the cells, not out.         ☐        ☐

e)  Carbon dioxide and water are transferred out of cells.           ☐        ☐

# The Heart and Circulation

**Q1**   Why is it very important for the heart to work efficiently?  Choose one answer from A-C.

A)  The heart working inefficiently would adversely affect the diffusion of substances from the appendix to the brain.  This could result in doxycycline lusions.

B)  The heart pumps blood to the body's organs.  If it was inefficient the organs wouldn't receive enough of the oxygen and glucose they need for respiration.

C)  The heart pumps blood to the body's organs.  If it was inefficient the organs wouldn't receive enough of the water and carbon they need for respiration.

**Q2**   Draw arrows on the diagram to show the direction of blood flow on both sides of the heart.

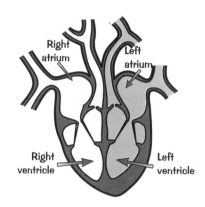

**Q3**   True or false?  *"The heart can be described as a double pump.  One side of the heart pumps blood to the lungs, the other side pumps blood to the rest of the body."*

**Q4**   Read the piece of writing and then answer the questions below.

Theories about the heart and circulation have changed a lot through the centuries.  Early theories, for example those of the Greek physician Galen (c.129-199 AD), were often incorrect.  Later theories based on experimentation and observation were more likely to be accurate and slowly replaced earlier theories.  For example, the English doctor William Harvey (1578-1657) used dissection and experiments to show that blood is pumped away from the heart in different vessels (arteries) from the ones it flows back in (veins).

a)  Why would theories based on experiment and observation be more likely to be accurate than theories based on imagination and persuasive argument?

b)  True or false?  *"It often took a long time for incorrect theories about blood circulation to be replaced with new theories."*

c)  Use the school library, Internet or other resources to find out more about William Harvey.  Write a paragraph on his ideas about the heart and circulation.

---

## Blood might be thicker than water, but it's still pretty clever...

Amazing stuff, blood.  Looks kinda red and useless when it comes spurting out of things in horror movies, but it's actually dead nifty.  It basically carries pretty much everything around your body that you need to live.  I mean — I need a huge great rucksack just for one weekend in Glastonbury.

*Unit 8B — Respiration*

# Respiration and Exercise

**Q1** True or false? *"Respiration means the same as breathing."*

**Q2** Complete the sentences by circling the right words.

The blood transports [oxygen / carbon dioxide] and [water / glucose] to the cells.
These substances are needed by the cells for the reaction of [oxidisation / respiration].
This reaction provides the cells with [electricity / energy]. Carbon dioxide is one waste
product of the reaction and passes out of the cells into the [lymphatic system / bloodstream].

**Q3** Write down three possible effects on the body of not getting
enough oxygen during exercise. Choose answers from options A-F.

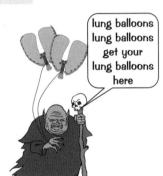

A) cramp/aching muscles

B) hunger

C) laziness

D) fainting

E) impaired hearing

F) fatigue

**Q4** Read the statements and then answer the questions.

The dictionary definition of aerobic is "relating to or requiring oxygen."

a) Why do you think "aerobic respiration" is so-called?

Respiration produces energy.

b) Why do people breathe in more air when they are exercising?

**Q5** Fill in the blanks.

a) Aerobic exercise is called that because it requires an increased intake of _____ .

b) An increased intake of _____ allows the person exercising to respire more.

c) The increased level of respiration produces more _____ .

**Q6** Name three situations where there might not be enough oxygen reaching the cells.

## Why do I breathe more during exercise? — cos I'm out of breath...

Know **why** your legs hurt if you run too fast? It's because you're not getting enough oxygen to
your muscles. Your body has to make energy somehow, so it breaks down glucose *without* using
oxygen. The result is a build-up of <u>lactic acid</u> in your muscles. It's no wonder they hurt, really.

# <u>*Role of the Lungs in Respiration*</u>

Q1     Copy this diagram and fill in the labels. Use the words in the box.

| bronchus | lung | trachea | ribs | heart | alveoli |

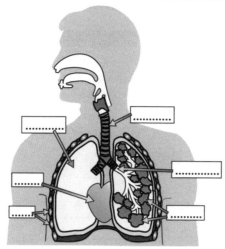

Q2     True or false? *"Inhaled air contains more carbon dioxide than exhaled air."*

Q3     Look at the diagram of the aveoli and then answer the questions below.

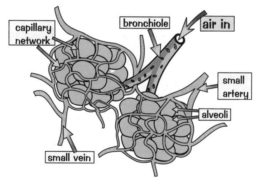

a)   What is the oxygen inhaled into the lungs used for?

b)   Mark onto the diagram the direction of oxygen between the blood capillaries and the alveoli.

c)   Using a different colour, mark on the direction of carbon dioxide between the blood capillaries and the alveoli.

d)   Why does the body produce carbon dioxide?

e)   Why do you think there are so many blood capillaries around the alveoli?

Q4     Name two features of the alveoli that make them efficient as surfaces for gas exchange.

Q5     The tar in cigarette smoke damages alveoli and reduces their ability to function. What effect would this have on gas exchange in the lungs?

# Respiration in other Living Organisms

Q1    The diagram shows an experiment to find out if different living organisms produce carbon dioxide. Copy the diagram and fill in the labels using the words in the box.

APPARATUS: transparent plastic dish with lid, stopwatch, gauze platform, measuring cylinder, lime water, maggots, germinating lentils

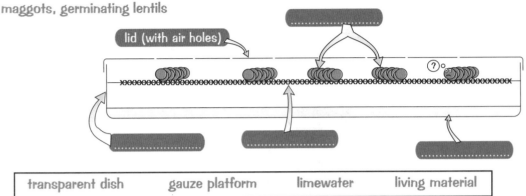

lid (with air holes)

| transparent dish | gauze platform | limewater | living material |

Q2    Read the text and then answer the questions below.

METHOD: We used a measuring cylinder to measure out 10cm³ lime water and put it into a transparent dish. A gauze platform was put on top of the dish. Ten maggots were put on the gauze platform and a lid with air holes was placed on top. After ten minutes we observed whether or not the lime water had turned cloudy. We repeated the experiment using 20 grams of germinating lentils and then again with no living material. Five groups in the class did the experiment. The results were put together into a single table.

a) Why was it necessary to have a control experiment where no living material was put on the gauze?

b) Why was it a good idea to repeat the experiment several times?

c) Which of the following options A-F are factors that needed to be controlled in the experiment?

A)    temperature                               D)    volume of living material

B)    volume of lime water                     E)    concentration of the lime water

C)    length of time before observed          F)    all of the above
      colour of limewater

Q3    Complete the sentences by circling the right words.

CONCLUSION: The limewater **turned cloudy / stayed clear** when maggots and germinating lentils were put on the gauze. This is because the maggots and lentils were **respiring / expiring** and producing carbon dioxide. We observed that the limewater turned cloudy more quickly if the maggots were **less active / more active**. This was because they were **respiring less / respiring more** to produce more energy and therefore, also more carbon dioxide. In the control test the limewater **turned cloudy / stayed clear** because there was no carbon dioxide being produced next to it. Overall, the results of the experiment suggest that both animals and **solids / plants** respire, producing carbon dioxide.

## <u>Micro-Organisms</u>

Q1    Copy and complete the sentence by picking the correct words from the box.

| microscope    large    smell    telescope    small    see |

Micro-organisms are so ................... that we can only ................... them when we use a ....................

Q2    Copy out the **correct** sentences from this list.

✦ Micro-organisms are all the same.

✦ All micro-organisms cause disease.

✦ Viruses, bacteria and fungi are types of micro-organisms.

✦ Viruses are much smaller than bacteria.

✦ Viruses produce antibiotics.

✦ Mushrooms, toadstools and yeast are all fungi.

✦ Many micro-organisms are useful.

Q3    Diagrams A, B and C represent different types of microorganism.  Copy each diagram and write down what type it is — bacteria, fungi or virus

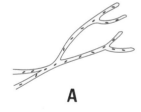

**Not drawn to scale.**

A                          B                          C

Q4    Copy this crossword and then use the clues to complete it.

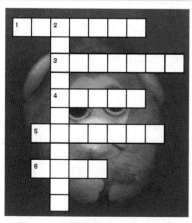

**Across**
1) Size of a virus compared to a bacterium.
3) Many fungi consist of long, fine tangled ...................
4) Yeast make this food rise.
5) Bacteria change milk into this tangy food.
6) Yeast and grape juice will make this.

**Down**
2) Fungi produce them and doctors prescribe them.

## <u>Eek, there's sommat strange lurking back there...</u>

Do you recognise the creature hiding behind the crossword?
Yes, that's right it's Jumbo Wilson's furry pet, Beatrice.

# Investigating Yeast

Q1    What is the name of the process that releases energy from food in every living organism?

Q2    During aerobic respiration (using oxygen), which gas is produced?

Q3    Bread is an important source of carbohydrate for many people.

    a) What name is given to uncooked bread?

    b) Which micro-organism is used to make bread?

    c) Bubbles of which gas make the uncooked bread rise?

    d) Why is sugar one of the ingredients of bread?

Q4    Johnny wants to know if temperature and amount of sugar affect respiration in yeast.
He sets up an experiment using the same amount of flour, yeast and water but changing the
temperature and amount of sugar. After one hour he compares the height of the dough.

    a) Which two cylinders should be compared to
       find out if temperature has an effect?

    b) Which two cylinders should be compared to
       find out if amount of sugar has an effect?

    c) Why is it necessary to use the same
       amount of yeast each time?

|  A  |  B  |  C  |  D  |
|-----|-----|-----|-----|
| Dough with 1g sugar 20 °C | Dough with 2g sugar 20 °C | Dough with 1g sugar 40 °C | Dough with 2g sugar 40 °C |

Q5    Johnny decides to investigate the effect of sugar on yeast
respiration in more detail. The table below shows his results.

| Mass of Sugar | Increase in height of dough (mm) | | |
|---------------|--------|--------|--------|
|               | Test 1 | Test 2 | Test 3 |
| 0.0 | 0 | 0 | 0 |
| 0.1 | 1 | 0 | 0 |
| 0.2 | 5 | 5 | 5 |
| 0.5 | 13 | 14 | 14 |
| 1.0 | 26 | 27 | 28 |
| 1.5 | 40 | 38 | 42 |
| 2.0 | 51 | 51 | 53 |

a) Plot a graph of mass of sugar against
**average** increase in height.

b) Describe the relationship between mass
of sugar and height of dough.

c) Describe the relationship between mass
of sugar and amount of carbon dioxide.

d) What is the relationship between amount of sugar and rate of respiration?

e) Why was it better to do the experiment more than once — so that he could
conclude that the results were i) fair  ii) reliable or iii) accurate?

# Growing Micro-organisms

**Q1**      Use these words to copy and complete the passage below.

| petri dish    agar    food    loop    streaked |
|---|
| water    nutrient    warmth    sterilised |

To grow bacteria in the laboratory they must be given ................, ............... and ...................

Many grow well on the surface of a jelly-like material called ................ Various food substances can be

added to the jelly to make ................ agar. The agar is sterilised and put into a shallow ................ ...................

Bacteria are ................ across the surface of the solid agar using a ................ wire ...................

**Q2**      When growing bacteria on agar, several safety precautions must be taken.
The words of three of these have been jumbled. Sort them out and write them correctly.

     a) laboratory a anything never in science eat

     b) working your bacteria with hands wash after always

     c) streaking after dish tape agar adhesive stick the around petri

**Q3**      Copy out these lists and draw lines to match
each product to the correct micro-organism.

| Product | Micro-organism |
|---|---|
| Yoghurt | Fungi |
| Quorn (mycoprotein) | Bacteria |
| Antibiotic | Yeast |
| Cheese | Fungi |
| Vinegar | Bacteria |
| Alcohol | Bacteria |

*I don't know how to tell you this old
chap, but it looks as though it's true...*

*...Margo has run
off with a microbe.*

**Q4**      Arrange these stages, of the production of cheese, into the correct order.

     **A**   Salt is added to the curds.

     **B**   The solid part of the curdled milk is separated from the liquid part (whey).

     **C**   Bacteria produce acid and make the milk go sour.

     **D**   Bacteria are allowed to ripen the cheese, softening it and giving it its characteristic smell and flavour.

     **E**   The milk curdles and goes lumpy.

# Micro-organisms can Cause Disease

**Q1**  A disease is a condition that prevents your body from working properly.
Write three sentences by matching the words on the left with the definitions on the right.

Infectious diseases          are organisms that cause disease.

Non-infectious diseases      are caused by organisms that can be passed on to other animals.

Pathogens                    can not be caught because they are not caused by organisms.

**Q2**  Which three of these diseases are infectious?

arthritis      influenza      tuberculosis      scurvy      polio      cancer

**Q3**  Copy and complete this table using the words in Doody's mouth:

| Infectious disease | Caused by |
|---|---|
| Rabies | |
| Common cold | |
| Tuberculosis | |
| Tetanus | |
| Food poisoning | |
| Whooping cough | |
| Athlete's foot | |
| Malaria | |

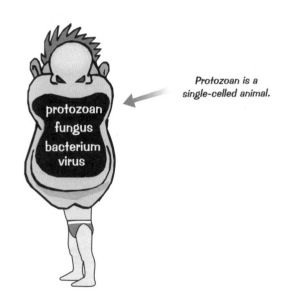

Protozoan is a single-celled animal.

protozoan
fungus
bacterium
virus

**Q4**  Rearrange these words to find three ways to avoid infections.

a) places avoid crowded

b) using after wash toilet hands your the

c) uncovered food never leave

**Q5**  Sort the diseases below into five lists as shown (some may appear in more than one list).

Sleeping sickness      Impetigo

Malaria      Food poisoning

Athlete's foot      Common cold

Dysentery      Chicken pox

Cholera      Rubella (German measles)

Typhoid

Tuberculosis      Whooping cough

| Spread by droplets in air | Spread by contact with others | Spread in food and water | Spread by insect and animal vectors | Passed across the placenta |
|---|---|---|---|---|
| | | | | |

# Preventing the Spread of Disease

Q1   Here's a rotten question to start you off...

a) Why does food rot?

b) What are the two main microbes that cause disease?

c) List 5 ways that disease can be spread.

d) What causes the symptoms of a disease — the **microbes** or the **toxins** produced by the microbes?

Q2   Copy and complete the following passage using the words in the box.

> Antiseptics   strong   disinfectants   cells   antibiotics

Drugs that kill microbes are called ................... . ................... are used to kill microbes on kitchen surfaces and in bathrooms. ................... are chemicals which kill microbes on living tissue. They are not as ................... as disinfectants, so don't damage your ................... .

Q3   Cholera is a serious bacterial infection.  It comes from drinking water or eating food contaminated with human sewage.  Cholera was common in the nineteenth century before the introduction of safe drinking water.  In 1849, Dr John Snow observed that the Cholera epidemic in London occurred mainly in regions served by the same water pump from Broad Street.  When he had the pump shut down, the epidemic subsided.

a) What type of micro-organism causes Cholera?

b) What causes a person to become infected with Cholera?

c) Explain why shutting down the water pumps in Broad Street stopped Cholera spreading.  (Hint: what do you think the pumps were infected with?)

d) What kind of places might you now expect cholera to occur?

Q4   List 4 ways you can prevent the spread of disease with good hygiene and explain how they help.

Q5   Answer these questions on sneezes and diseases...

a) Why should you cover your mouth with a tissue when you sneeze?

b) What are the differences between bacteria and viruses?

c) How does improved sanitation help prevent the spread of disease?

d) What is pasteurisation?

## Bring out your dead, bring out your dead...

A lot of micro-organisms are pretty evil, and there are loads of ways they can infect you — eating, insect bites, even just breathing... it's all pretty scary.  So here's what you should do: learn all the <u>diseases</u>, how they <u>spread</u> and what we can do to prevent <u>them</u>. (E.g. having a wash every now and then is always a good one...)

# _Natural Barriers_

**Q1** Copy and match up the following natural barriers with how they protect you from infection.

| Barrier | Protection |
| --- | --- |
| • Tears | • produce mucus to trap microbes and dust. Tiny hairs push mucus up to be swallowed. |
| • Scabs | • are antiseptic to kill microbes. |
| • Skin | • contains acid to kill microbes. |
| • Lungs | • forms a barrier to germs and has glands that produce an antiseptic oil. |
| • Stomach | • form a barrier to stop germs from getting into the blood. |

**Q2** Copy out the following sentences in the correct order.

**A** Your white blood cells produce antibodies that stick the invading
bacteria together, making it easier for white blood cells to attack them.

**B** You are now immune to this type of harmful bacteria.

**C** Harmful bacteria enter your body through a cut.

**D** Antibodies stay in the blood to fight off future infection.

**Q3** Some of the statements below are wrong. Copy them all out, correcting the false ones.

a) Different micro-organisms that cause disease need different types of antibodies to attack them.

b) White blood cells, called phagocytes, engulf invading microbes and digest them.

c) People always get ill when exposed to potentially dangerous micro-organisms.

d) Antibodies produced by white blood cells can also neutralise poisons.

**Q4** Answer these questions.

a) What piece of equipment do you use to look at microbes?

b) Briefly describe the processes that invading bacteria undergo when
they infect your body and make you ill.

c) What is the job of antitoxins made by white blood cells?

---

## _If only England's defence were this well organised..._

So there's three ways nasty organisms get into our bodies: through the <u>skin</u>, by <u>eating and drinking</u> and by <u>breathing</u>. Our bodies have natural defences against all of these — learn them. White blood cells are well <u>funky</u>, they <u>eat</u> invading cells and produce <u>antibodies</u> and <u>antitoxins</u> — not bad for a microscopic <u>cell</u>.

---

_Unit 8C — Microbes and Disease_

# Medicines

**Q1**    Answer the following questions.

a) Give some examples of common household anti-microbial products.

b) What jelly-like substance can you grow microbes on in the lab?

c) What does inoculate mean?

d) Why would bacteria not grow on an agar plate treated with a disinfectant?

**Q2**    Copy these sentences, choosing the correct words.

a) [Penicillin / Paracetemol] can only be obtained on prescription.

b) Antibiotics have been very successful in the [treatment / cause] of disease.

c) [All / Not all] drugs are antibiotics.

d) The discovery of penicillin was [planned / an accident].

**Q3**    Copy and complete the following paragraph using words from the box.

> antibiotic   chemicals   kills   bacteria.

Antibiotics only work on ................... .  Some medicines that are not ................... work by suppressing the symptoms of the illness.  Symptoms are the body's response to the waste ................... made by the microbes.  An antibiotic ................... microbes that cause the symptoms.

**Q4**    Here's one to test your history knowledge:

a) Which famous scientist discovered *Pennicillium notatum*?

b) How did Howard Florey save millions of lives?

c) Why do antibiotics not work on all bacteria?

d) Why do doctors try to limit the use of antibiotics?

e) Why would antibiotics not help you if you had the flu?

*Good Lord!  That's no microbe, that's Gerald with a phoney moustache!*

---

## Episode III — Attack of the Bacteria...

Scene 1 — lots of horrid bacteria make everyone ill.  Scene 2 — some dude called Alexander finds some blue mould on his toast.  He calls it penicillium.  The world is saved.  **THE END.**  (I think it needs a twist or something...)

# Immunisation

Q1    Copy and complete the passage choosing the correct words from the box.

kill,  bacteria,  immunised,  injection,   immunisation.

TB is a harmful disease.  When you are in secondary school you have an ................. .

This is known as the BCG.  You are vaccinated with a dead form of the ................. which

causes the disease.  If you are not ................. and you catch this disease, it can .................

you.  ................. saves thousands of lives and millions of pounds for the health service.

Q2    Now, copy out and complete this passage using the words in the box.

placenta    immunity    vaccines    quickly    antibodies    breast milk

When it is a fetus a baby receives ................. from its mother through the ................. .

After the baby is born it continues to receive antibodies from the mother from ................. .

Later in childhood the baby can be injected with ................. .  These build up ................. to

certain diseases.  When you are immune to a disease your body can ................. make the

antibodies needed to fight off that disease.

Q3    Answer the following questions about vaccines.

a) Explain how the National Health Service has helped to reduce childhood diseases.

b) A vaccine contains dead or weakened forms of the disease it prevents. True or false?

c) What does MMR stand for?

Q4    Some of these statements are incorrect.  Copy them all out, correcting the false ones.

a) Viruses can cause diseases.

b) Microbes cannot infect open wounds.

c) Pasteur was the first surgeon to use antiseptics in operations.

d) Microbes spread slowly in overcrowded conditions.

e) Your white blood cells help to protect you from disease.

f) Penicillin stops bacteria from reproducing.

g) Once you have had measles you are immune and can catch it again.

h) Antibodies in your blood help to form scabs when you cut yourself.

i) Bacteria can sometime be useful rather than cause disease.

# Classification

Q1    a)  What is an organism's habitat?

b)  Which habitats do these animals belong to?  (Choose from the grey box.)

**Crab**        **Beetle**        **Deer**        **Frog**

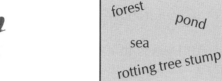

forest
pond
sea
rotting tree stump

c) What does a plant need to survive in its habitat?

d) What decides whether a living thing is a plant or an animal?    *Hint: it's to do with food.*

Q2    Copy and complete the passage using words from the grey box.

> mammals      invertebrates      flatworms      arthropods      legs
> amphibians      vertebrates      molluscs      segmented worms

Animals with backbones are called ................. . There are five smaller groups of animals with backbones.

These are birds, ................. , fish, ................. and reptiles.  Animals without backbones are called

................. . These can be sub-divided into cnidarians, ................. , roundworms, ................. ,

echinoderms ................. , and ................. . Arthropods are a group that have jointed ................. .

Q3    Write out each vertebrate group from the left with the correct characteristic from the right.

| FISH | covered in feathers, lay eggs and are warm-blooded. |
| MAMMALS | young live in water as tadpoles and have gills. Adults live on land and have lungs. |
| REPTILES | live in water and have gills. They are cold-blooded. |
| AMPHIBIANS | have hair, give birth to live young and feed them on milk.  They are warm-blooded. |
| BIRDS | have a dry, scaly, waterproof skin. They are cold-blooded and lay eggs on land. |

Q4    There are two kinds of plants, those which make spores, and those that produce seeds.
These are divided further into ferns, mosses/liverworts, flowering plants and conifers.

a) *Name the category of plants that:* produce spores, have weak roots, thin delicate leaves
and live in damp places.

b) *Name the category of plants that:* produce spores, have tubes called xylem to transport
water and have strong stems, roots and leaves.

c) *Name the category of plants that:* are evergreen, with leaves like needles, containing xylem
but without flowers.

# Habitat Data Collection

Q1  Pooters, quadrats, sweep nets, pitfall traps, kick samples, dipping nets and tree beating are methods of sampling organisms from different habitats. Which methods would you use for sampling the organisms in the following habitats?

   a) invertebrates in grassland          b) life in a pond          c) invertebrates in a stream

   d) insects in a hedgerow          e) plant species in a meadow          f) invertebrates in a tree canopy

Q2  Answer these questions about habitats.

   a)  Describe the main difference between an aquatic habitat and a terrestrial habitat.

   b)  List the environmental data you would collect about an aquatic habitat and a terrestrial habitat.

   c)  Suggest a reason why communities differ in different habitats.

   d)  Why might you want to measure populations in a river downstream of a factory?

   e)  Why would you measure populations more than once a year?

   f)  Why might you take more than one quadrat when sampling grasses on the school field?

Q3  Look at this table and then answer questions a) to c).

   a) Draw a graph to present the following data on rainfall.

Don't you just hate chainsaw rain.

| Month | Rainfall (mm) |
|-------|---------------|
| Jan | 57 |
| Feb | 80 |
| Mar | 130 |
| Apr | 180 |
| May | 65 |
| Jun | 30 |
| Jul | 35 |
| Aug | 0 |
| Sept | 5 |
| Oct | 70 |
| Nov | 80 |
| Dec | 65 |

   b) Describe the rainfall during August and September.

   c) Suggest one way this could affect populations of organisms living in this habitat.

## Tree beating — this is where biologists started to lose the plot...

Yep, whoever invented this stuff was a complete nutcase, I mean look at these names:  pooters, pitfall traps, kick sampling, dipping, tree beating...  Anyway, go and hassle your teacher to show you all these methods.  Biology doesn't get any better than bug-collecting fun like this...

# Communities and Organisms

**Q1**   For each group of organisms below write out all those that belong in the same community.  Then say which habitat they live in (choose from the grey box).

a) Grass, centipede, beetle, grasshopper, perch.

b) Hedgehog, oak trees, vole, camel, owl.

c) Mussels, algae, blackbird, flatfish, starfish.

rock pool

meadow

woodland

**Q2**   Identify organisms A to E using the following key.

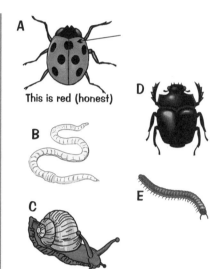

**KEY:**

1.   a. The organism has jointed legs............................ Go to 2
     b. The organism has no legs................................ Go to 4

2.   a. The organism has 6 legs.................................Go to 3
     b. The organism has more than 6 legs....................Millipede

3.   a. The organism is red with black spots......................Ladybird
     b. The organism is black........................................Beetle

4 .   a. The organism has a shell..................................... Snail
     b. no shell .......................................................Earthworm

A

This is red (honest)

B

C

D

E

**Q3**   Look at the two habitats below with the lists of the organisms that live in them.  Then answer the questions.

| **POND** | **OAK TREE** |
| --- | --- |
| Freshwater shrimp | Snail |
| Pond snail | Spider |
| Newt | Aphid |
| Pond Skater | Centipede |
| Water Beetle | Caterpillar |
| Mayfly Nymph | Ladybird |

a) How would you collect the organisms from the different habitats?

b) Why are the communities different even though the habitat could be in the same area?

c) What kind of chart would you use to present data on the number of these organisms?

*Unit 8D — Ecological Relationships*

# Environmental Conditions

Q1    Copy out each apparatus below followed by the environmental factor it measures.

| Apparatus | Environmental factor |
|-----------|---------------------|
| Flowmeter | acidity of river water |
| Oxygen probe | intensity of the sunlight |
| Light sensor | dissolved oxygen |
| Temperature probe | speed of a stream |
| pH probe | temperature |

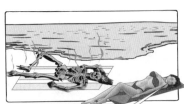

Turn over Griff you're starting to burn.

Q2    Briefly outline one way you could measure temperature variation in a pond over a period of 24 hours, using ICT.

Q3    Copy and complete the following passage using the words from the grey box.

> increased    oxygen    daytime    plants    fewer    warmed    different    colder    block

Ponds support a variety of life. The water is still and gets easily ................ by the sun

in the ................ . The ................ grow well but can ................ out the sunlight to the

lower levels, resulting in low ................ levels.  In streams and rivers, conditions

are ................ to ponds.  The fast flowing water is ................ and there

are ................ plants.  When the water flows over the rocks, oxygen levels

are ................ by aeration.

Q4    a) What environmental conditions influence the types of organism living in these habitats?

   i) Arctic tundra       ii) Desert        iii) Rock pool           iv) River

b) What does it mean when an animal is said to be "adapted to its environment"?

c) Describe how a polar bear is adapted to live in the cold conditions in the Arctic.

d) Why is it important that animals and plants are adapted to their surroundings?

## ICT and when ICT I drinks it...

You can use ICT datalogging equipment to collect <u>environmental</u> data.  It's a great way to compare conditions in different habitats — which helps you <u>understand</u> the things living there — how they are adapted to the environmental conditions and all that business...

# Population Size

Q1    Answer these questions about populations.

a) What is a population?

b) Why do animals live together in populations?

c) What kind of apparatus would you use to count and
   find out about weeds on the school field?

Q2    Copy and complete the following paragraph using the words from the grey box.

| burrow    nesting sites    light    predators    water    nutrients    resources |
|---|

The size of a population can be limited by ................... , ................... and ................... .

Other animals may need more ............... , e.g. birds also need ............... , and rabbits

need a ............... to hide from ............... .

Q3    Copy and complete the table.

| Limiting factor | In what way does it limit a population? (Give a reason) |
|---|---|
| Light | |
| Climate | |
| Predators | |
| Shelter | |
| Space | |
| Food | |
| Water | |
| Oxygen | |
| Disease | |

Q4    Copy out these statements about predator and prey populations in the correct order.

A With fewer predators the prey has a chance to survive and reproduce, the prey numbers
   increase and the cycle begins again.

B Predators move into the area, to eat the prey.  They eat well and reproduce.

C Prey move into an area and they have lots of food.
   They reproduce rapidly and become high in numbers.

D Fewer prey mean less food for the predators.  Some die of starvation and their numbers fall.

E Lots of predators eat lots of prey so the numbers of prey fall.

# _Feeding Relationships_

Q1     a) Arrange the organisms on the right correctly into a food chain.

b) Which organism is a producer?

c) Which organism is a herbivore?

d) Which organism is a secondary consumer?

e) Which organisms are carnivores?

f) What do the arrows mean in a food chain?

g) Where does the energy come from in a food chain?

**Algae**

**Pike**

**Tadpole**

**Stickleback**

Q2     Look at this food web.

a) Why is a food web better than a food chain?

b) How many food chains can you
   find in this food web?

c) What would happen to the
   number of ladybirds if the
   aphids disappeared?

d) What would happen to the number
   of hawks, caterpillars and ladybirds
   if the blackbirds disappeared?

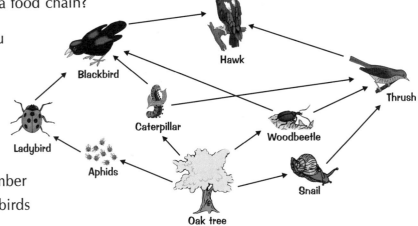

Hawk

Blackbird

Thrush

Caterpillar

Woodbeetle

Ladybird

Aphids

Snail

Oak tree

Q3     a) What is a pyramid of numbers?

b) Draw pyramids of numbers for the following food chains.

   i) Grass seed ➙ chaffinch ➙ Buzzard

   ii) Oak tree ➙ Caterpillars ➙ Blackbirds ➙ Hawk ➙ Fleas

Q4     Copy and complete the passage.

When organisms die their bodies are broken down by d＿＿＿＿＿ . These decomposers release

n＿＿＿＿＿ back into the soil.  P＿＿＿＿＿ can then use these chemicals in their g＿＿＿＿＿ .

> # _I was a herbivore the operation — but now you can call me Dave..._
> **The arrow points _FROM_ the food _TO_ the eater.**
>
>                 ...not the other way round.  That's all you need to remember.  <u>Don't forget</u> it.

# Materials and Elements

**Q1** Which of the following are **materials**?

a) chair    f) tree

b) glass    g) polystyrene

c) iodine    h) horse

d) wood    i) PVC

e) egg    j) gold

**Q2** Name at least five different materials that you can see in the room where you are right now.

**Q3** Which of the following objects are made from just one element?

a) copper wire    e) platinum ring

b) wooden spoon    f) glass jar

c) rubber hose    g) titanium bolt

d) gold bar    h) aluminium saucepan

**Q4** Which of the following are elements?

a) wood    g) carbon

b) marble    h) sugar

c) iron    i) polythene

d) copper    j) brass

e) rubber    k) chlorine

f) zinc    l) paper

**Q5** Are there any materials which aren't made up of elements?

**Q6** Roughly how many elements are there?

---

## Matt Erial and Elle Ment — what a lovely couple...

There's not a heck of a lot to this page — you just need to know your elements and what materials and elements are. Simple, but deadly important for the rest of this book so get them sorted.

# *Element Structure*

Q1    Which of these building-brick structures is like an element?

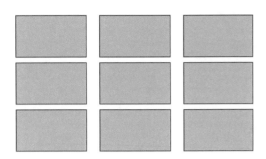
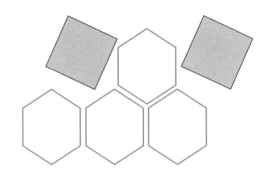

Q2    If you pulled a lump of an element apart again and again you'd eventually be left with **very small particles** that **couldn't** be pulled apart any more.  What are these particles **called**?

a) bricks    b) atoms    c) grains    d) bits

Q3    Copy these diagrams and label the atoms in each one.  Say whether each one is a mixture, element or compound.  The first one has already been done.

a)
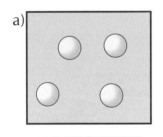

| Element |
| --- |

b)
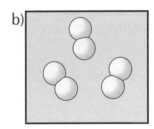

................

c)
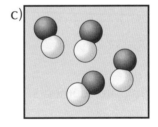

................

d)
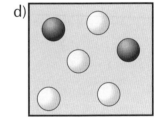

................

Q4    Is the material in diagram d) in Q3 an element or not?  How do you know?

Q5    All elements have a symbol, which is like a shorthand for their name.
Match up these chemical symbols with what they stand for.

a)    S                          i)     carbon

b)    N                          ii)    oxygen

c)    O                          iii)   iron

d)    C                          iv)    sulfur

e)    Fe                         v)     sodium

f)    Na                         vi)    nitrogen

# *Types of Element*

Read this table about 7 elements carefully. You need it for the first two questions.

| iron | Fe | metal | magnetic |
|------|-----|-----------|--------------|
| copper | Cu | metal | non-magnetic |
| oxygen | O | non-metal | non-magnetic |
| nitrogen | N | non-metal | non-magnetic |
| sulfur | S | non-metal | non-magnetic |
| titanium | Ti | metal | non-magnetic |
| sodium | Na | metal | non-magnetic |

Q1    Name the elements which are **metals**.

Q2    Are **most** of the metals magnetic or non-magnetic?

Q3    Which of these elements are **gases** at 20°C?

Q4    Where could you look to find out more information about any of these elements?

Q5    Look at the periodic table below. Where are the metals on the table — on the left hand side or the right hand side?

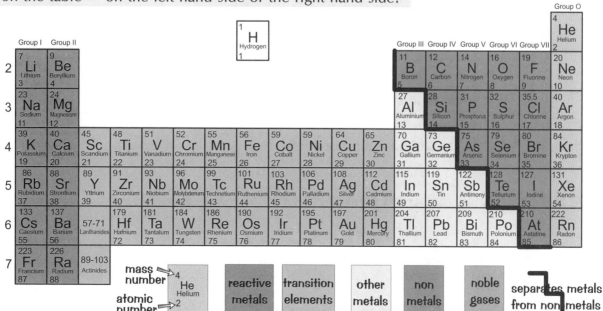

---

# *Don't panic — it's only everything the universe is made from...*

The periodic table shows all the elements with similar elements listed close together. You don't need to know a great deal about all the elements, only some of them. You do need to know how to find out information from the table and how to understand the information.

# Types of Element

Q1    Which of these statements are true, and which are false?

a) Argon is an element.

b) Water is an element.

c) Wood is only made of one type of atom.

d) Far fewer materials are elements than are not elements.

e) Water is made of hydrogen and oxygen atoms.

f)  Carbon is made of only one type of atom.

g) There are over a thousand elements.

Q2    Copy this table, and use any resources you like (internet, CD-rom, books) to fill it in.

| Element | Symbol | State at 20°C | Metal/non-metal |
|---------|--------|---------------|-----------------|
| Cadmium |        |               |                 |
|         | K      |               |                 |
| Fluorine |       |               |                 |
| Silicon |        |               |                 |

Use a periodic table, and any other resources (including research you've done in class) to help you answer the next few questions.

Q3    Where on the periodic table are the non-metals?

Q4    Are there any metals that **aren't** solid at 20°C?  If so, name them.

Q5    Which non-metal is a liquid at 20°C?

Q6    Where on the periodic table are the elements which are gases at 20°C?

Q7    Which elements are magnetic?

# Compounds and Molecules

**Q1**   What's the name for a material made of atoms of different elements combined together?

**Q2**   What's the name for a particle made of atoms joined together?

**Q3**   Which of these are made from different atoms joined together?

a) water

b) salt

c) carbon

d) baking soda

Everyone's made up of atoms — even Disney characters like me.

**Q4**   Name the elements that are joined together to make these compounds:

a) water

b) carbon dioxide

c) sodium iodide

**Q5**   Look at these diagrams, and answer the questions below.

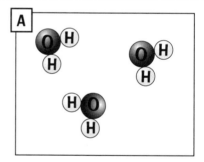

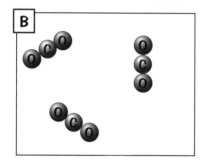

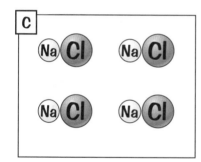

a) Which diagram shows water?

b) Which diagram shows carbon dioxide?

c) How many atoms of oxygen are there in a molecule of water?

**Q6**   Match these pictures of models of molecules to the correct names from the box.

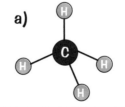

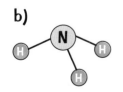

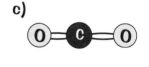

ammonia

methane

carbon dioxide

## Molecules — kinda like Hercules with a taste for worms...

There are squillions of materials in the universe, like wood, glass, water, fingernails, baking powder, the list goes on and on. Atoms of elements join together to make molecules. Loads of molecules make compounds. Different compounds and mixes of compounds make up materials. Simple.

# Compounds and Molecules

**Q1** Water is made of one atom of oxygen joined to two atoms of hydrogen.

   a) What is the name for one particle of water?

   b) Describe in terms of atoms what happens when hydrogen and oxygen react to make water.

   c) Are hydrogen and oxygen solids, gases or liquids at 20°C?

   d) Is water a solid, a liquid or a gas at 20°C?

**Q2** Sodium chloride is made of atoms of sodium joined to atoms of chlorine.

   a) What is sodium like at 20°C?  Describe its appearance.

   b) What is chlorine like at 20°C?  Describe its appearance.

   c) What is sodium chloride like at 20°C? Describe its appearance.

**Q3** Write down the **word equations** for the reactions between these elements:

   a) hydrogen and oxygen

   b) iron and sulfur

   c) sodium and iodine

   d) silver and chlorine

   e) lithium and oxygen

   f) magnesium and oxygen

**Q4** Sketch rough diagrams to show the following:

*Hint: the rough diagrams only need to be circles with the element's symbol in them.*

   a) One oxygen atom

   b) Two separate hydrogen atoms

   c) One water molecule (one atom of oxygen joined to two atoms of hydrogen)

   d) Now put the diagrams from a), b) and c) together with a plus sign and an arrow in between, to make a picture equation for the formation of water from hydrogen and oxygen.

**Q5** Water can be broken down into its elements by electrolysis.

   a) When water is electrolysed, bubbles of gas are formed.
   What elements do these bubbles consist of?

   b) Electrolysis means breaking a compound down using... what?

# Simple Chemical Reactions

Q1    Read about this experiment, and then answer the questions below.

> Joseph heats a strip of zinc strongly
> in air, over a bunsen burner. The
> surface of the zinc becomes white.
> A white powder is quickly formed.

a) What is the chemical name of this white powder?

b) Write the word equation for the reaction.

c) When Joseph has finished heating the zinc strip, what should he do to the bunsen burner?

d) What should Joseph use to hold the zinc strip in the bunsen flame?

e) What is the hottest part of the blue bunsen flame?

Q2    Why is it dangerous to wander off and leave a bunsen burner on the blue flame?

Q3    When you're doing practical work in the science lab, where should these things be?

a) Your bag.

b) Your freakishly long hair.

Q4    For each of the following compounds, say which two elements it's made from.

a) copper oxide                    d) chromium oxide

b) silver chloride                  e) sodium fluoride

c) carbon dioxide                  f) iron chloride

Q5    For each of the compounds say which two elements it's made from.

a) $NaCl$                          d) $Ag(Br)_2$

b) $FeBr_2$                        e) $CuO$

c) $MgO$                          f) $CaCl_2$

## Dog in a tent — he's a camp hound...

These compounds aren't too hard, to be honest. Get used to those chemical symbols — the more
you use them, the easier it gets. Questions on safety rules in the lab keep cropping up, so get them
learned for simple marks, oh yeah and they'll also stop you getting hideously burned or something.

*Unit 8E — Atoms and Elements*

# Element or Not?

Q1    Read the following sentences carefully.
Do they describe an element, a
non-element, or is it impossible to tell?

a) It's made of tiny particles called atoms.

b) It's made of different kinds of atoms joined together.

c) It's water.

d) This substance has the formula NaCl.

e) This substance has the formula $N_2$.

f) This substance gives off a gas when it is heated.

I'm in my non-element when I'm in the water.

Q2    These are slightly harder.  Again, is it an
element or not, or is it impossible to tell?

a) This substance has the chemical symbol C.

b) This chemical has the chemical symbol Cu.

c) This substance has the chemical formula CuO.

d) This substance has the chemical symbol Pb.

Q3    **13g** of **substance X**, a shiny solid, was heated over a Bunsen burner.
It turned into a white powder. The white powder had a mass of **19g**.

a) What two changes occurred after heating substance X?

b) Why do you think each of those changes might have occurred?

Q4    420g of calcium carbonate was heated. It was
weighed afterwards and was found to have lost mass.

a) Write down two possible explanations for why it lost mass.

b) How might you try to find out which explanation was the correct one?

## *You could drive yourself ele-mental with this...*

This page tests if you know your stuff about elements and non-elements.  If you get any wrong,
research the answer, try them again, and keep trying until you get them all right.

# Compounds and Formulas

**Q1**  Here are descriptions of some materials, together with the number of each type of atom they're made of, and their chemical formula.  Match them up.  Easy...

Description:                One particle of this material is made of:                Formula:

A colourless gas

Two atoms of oxygen joined together                $CO_2$

A white solid

Two atoms of chlorine joined together               $H_2O$

A colourless liquid

One atom of carbon joined to two atoms of oxygen    $O_2$

A colourless gas

One atom of zinc joined to one atom of oxygen        $Cl_2$

A greenish gas that
smells of swimming pools

Two atoms of hydrogen joined to one atom of oxygen   $ZnO$

**Q2**  How many atoms of **oxygen** are there in each of these compounds?

a) $CuO$               d) $Li_2O$

b) $H_2O$              e) $H_2SO_4$        *Hmmm... those little numbers must mean __something__...*

c) $MnO_2$             f) $CaCO_3$

**Q3**  Which **elements** are in these compounds, and **how many atoms** of each element are there in each compound?

a) $FeCl_2$            g) $CaCO_3$

b) $NaBr$             h) $H_2SO_4$        *Use a Periodic Table to help you with the chemical symbols*

c) $ZnCl_2$            i) $AlCl_3$

d) $MgO$             j) $NH_4Cl$

e) $NH_3$             k) $Fe_2O_3$

f) $HNO_3$            l) $KMnO_4$

## Old MacDonald had a Formula...
A __formula__ tells you __how many__ atoms of each element there are in a substance.  It's easy once you get used to it.  The chemical symbols do take a bit of learning — so use your Periodic Table.

# <u>*Compounds and their Components*</u>

Q1    Read the description of a chemical reaction carried out
by a student, and answer the questions underneath.

> Anita heated some yellow **sulfur powder** and some dark
> grey **iron filings** together in a test tube.  When the contents
> of the tube glowed orange, she took the test tube off the
> flame and put it in a cooling rack.  After it had cooled, she
> emptied the test tube onto a piece of paper.  The contents
> of the test tube had turned into a grey lumpy solid, which
> wasn't attracted to a magnet.  Anita couldn't get either
> sulfur powder or iron filings out of the grey lump.

a) After being heated, does the test tube still contain a mixture of
sulfur and iron, or has a new compound been formed?

b) Why can't Anita separate the grey lump into yellow sulfur
powder and dark grey iron filings?

c) Do you think the grey lump would react with acid in the same
way that iron reacts with acid?

Q2    Read the following exciting facts, then answer the question underneath.

i)     Oxygen is a colourless gas at 20°C.

ii)    Carbon is a black solid at 20°C.

iii)   Hydrogen is a colourless gas at 20°C.

iv)    Water is a compound.  Each water molecule is made of two hydrogen
atoms joined to one oxygen atom.  Water is a clear liquid at 20°C.

v)     Each molecule of carbon dioxide is made of two oxygen atoms joined to
one carbon atom.  Carbon dioxide is a colourless gas at 20°C.

a) Do compounds have similar properties to the elements they're made from?

b) Are all water molecules identical, or are some of them different?

Q3    The formula for calcium chloride is $CaCl_2$.  How many more chlorine
atoms are there than copper atoms in one kilogram of calcium chloride?

a) Twice as many      b) Half as many      c) Three times as many

# Do Compounds React Chemically?

**Q1**  Answer the questions on heating sucrose below.

a) Describe the changes that happen when sugar (sucrose) is heated.

b) How does the end product of heating sucrose strongly compare with some unheated sucrose?  Do you think they are the same material?
Why do you think they are/aren't the same material?

c) Do you think a chemical reaction has happened?  Explain your answer.

**Q2**  Clear dilute ammonia solution is gradually added to blue copper sulphate solution.
The liquid in the beaker goes paler and cloudy.  A pale blue solid settles to the bottom.

a) Do you think a chemical reaction has happened here?

b) How can you tell?  What's the evidence?

**Q3**  Name **four** different kinds of evidence that show you a chemical reaction has taken place.  Think about what changes you would see.

**Q4**  When something **burns**, what element in the air is it reacting with?

**Q5**  Time for some fill-in-the gaps questions.  Copy out the sentences, and fill in the gaps using **some** of the words from the grey box.

> ELEMENTS    COMPOUNDS    FORMULA
>
> MOLECULES    COMPOUND    RUCKSACK
>
> ELEMENT    MIXTURE    ATOMS

a)  .................... are made of just one sort of atom.

b)  The ................. in two different elements can join together in a chemical reaction.

c)  A molecule of a ................. is made of different atoms joined together.

d)  You can tell what elements are in a compound by looking at the symbols in its

.................... .

# Mixtures

Q1 Which of these diagrams show **compounds** and which show **mixtures**?

a) 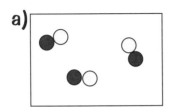  b) 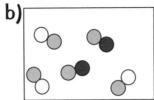  c) 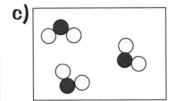  d)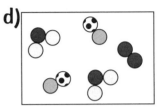

Q2 Name four "everyday" mixtures.

*eg seawater...*

Q3 Is the following statement true or false? *"The different particles in a mixture aren't in fixed proportions. This means the amounts of the different ingredients in a mixture can vary."*

Q4 How would you **separate** the following mixtures?

a) sugar dissolved in water

b) the different dyes in blue ink

c) iron filings and sulfur powder

This is DJ Mad Prof in the mix.

Q5 Air is a **mixture** of gases. Name four gases present in air, and give rough % proportions for each of them.

Q6 Give uses for two different gases present in air.

Q7 The body **uses oxygen** and **produces carbon dioxide**. How do you think the air you **breathe out** might be **different** from the air you **breathe in**?

Q8 A **pure** compound contains **only** molecules of that compound, and nothing else. Is there such a thing as a **pure mixture**?

---

## Fatboy science — mesyricht — it's a chemistry remix...

Lots of materials are <u>mixtures</u>, made of different kinds of particle mixed up together. The particles in a mixture <u>aren't</u> chemically joined together like the particles in a compound. This means you can separate the particles in a mixture. So get back to that pile of salt and sand Cinderella.

# Melting and Boiling Points

**Q1** Look at the table of melting points and boiling points, and answer the questions below.

|  | Melting Point | Boiling Point |
|---|---|---|
| Iron | 1535°c | 2750°c |
| Sodium | 97.8°c | 552.9°c |
| Chlorine | -100.98°c | -34.6°c |
| Sodium chloride | 801°c | 1413°c |
| Ammonia | -78.3°c | -33°c |

a) Which column tells you the freezing point of the material?

b) Is ammonia a solid, a liquid or a gas at 20°C?

c) Is the boiling point always higher than the melting point?

d) Will all lumps of pure iron always melt at the same temperature?

e) Will all pure ammonia always boil at the same temperature?

**Q2** What is the link between **freezing** and **melting**?

**Q3** The melting point of nitrogen is -210°C. The boiling point of nitrogen is -196°C. What can you say about the temperature of liquid nitrogen?

**Q4** Does air have a fixed boiling point? If yes, what is it? If not, explain why not.

**Q5** Read the following (true) statements, and answer the questions below.

> Pure water boils at 100°C. It stays at 100°C while it boils.
>
> Salt solution boils at a slightly higher temperature, and the temperature increases slightly as it boils.

a) Is salt solution a **pure** substance or a **mixture**?

b) Do mixtures have fixed boiling points or not?

---

**Mel Ting and Bo I Ling — they'll never meet...** *(these jokes are getting a bit samey)*
Elements and compounds don't freeze and boil at any old temperature, you know. They have their own fixed melting and boiling points. Mixtures on the other hand — they're all over the shop.

# Elements, Compounds and Mixtures

Q1    Read the paragraph about the experiment, and answer the questions underneath.

> Harold makes three different solutions of common salt (sodium chloride).
> Solution A has 1 g of salt per 100 ml, solution B has 5 g of salt per 100
> ml, and solution C has 10 g of salt per 100 ml.  He measures the melting
> point of each solution as he cools them and records the results.

Solution A started to freeze at –0.5°C.  Solution B started to freeze at –2°C.
Solution C started to freeze at –6°C.

a) How does the melting point vary with the strength of the solution?

b) Salt solution is a mixture of two compounds — sodium chloride and water.
From this experiment, can you say whether mixtures have a fixed melting point or not?

Q2    Look at these graphs of two liquids cooling.  Which liquid is a pure liquid?

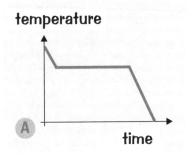

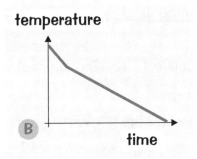

*Pure liquids have a single melting point but mixtures melt over a range of temperatures.*

Q3    Write out these statements.  After each one, write **element** if it's true of elements,
**compound** if it's true of compounds, and **mixture** if it's true of mixtures.

a) It's made of different types of atoms joined together chemically.

b) It's made of just one type of atom.                    *Some statements will fit into more than one
                                                            category.  Easy enough — so off you go.*

c) It's made up of just one type of molecule.

d) It can be represented by a chemical formula.

e) Its composition never varies.

f) It's made of different types of particle mixed up together, and you can separate the
components out by chromotography or distillation.

g) It doesn't have a definite, fixed boiling point.

# Rock Properties

**Q1** If you were given ten different rock samples, and had to sort them into groups, which of the following properties would make a **good scientific basis** for sorting the rocks?

     a) texture

       b) colour

         c) size of grains

           d) density

             e)  shape

I'd check the 'best before' on that if I were you Malcolm.

**Q2** Read about the experiment, then answer the questions.

> A piece of granite and a piece of sandstone were weighed, then placed in water for a minute, taken out and weighed again. The granite **did not change** in mass, but the **wet** sandstone weighed **more** than the **dry** sandstone.

a) Why did the wet sandstone weigh more than the dry sandstone?

b) The sandstone bubbled slightly as it went underwater. Why?

c) What's the scientific term for rocks that let water in?

**Q3** Is **smooth, shiny** rock or **dull, grainy looking** rock more likely to let water pass through it?

**Q4** Which of these diagrams shows **non-porous** rock?

**a)**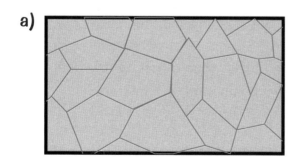

**b)**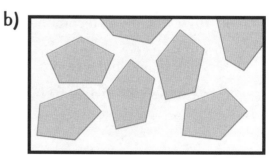

## Rock-a-doodle-do...

Always good for a laugh, are rocks. They come in all kinds of different textures and colours. You could build a horse out of rock — or a house for that matter. Learn the properties, move on.

# Biological and Chemical Weathering

Q1    Look at these pictures of statues.  How does rock on the
**brand new** statue compare to rock on the **old statue**?

**Posh Spice
(c. 2002 A.D.)**

**Posh Spice-ugh
(c. 876 B.C.)**

Q2    How can **plants** cause weathering and cracking in rock?

Q3    All rainwater is slightly acidic.  If you added a few drops of **universal
indicator** to rainwater, what colour would you expect it to go?

Q4    Read about this experiment, then answer the questions.

> You can simulate the action of acidic rainwater on rock by
> placing a lump of granite in a bath of dilute hydrochloric
> acid. The reaction between the granite and the acid is very
> slow and gradual.  You would need to check the
> appearance of the granite once a day for at least a week.

a) **How** would you record the very slow, gradual changes in the piece of granite?

b) Some grains in the granite dissolve more quickly than others.  What does this tell
you about the granite — is it likely to be a **compound** or a **mixture**?

---

**_Don't Weathering Frodo, don't weathering..._** *(sorry, bad jokes are just a hobbit of mine)*

Acid rain, tree roots, bits getting knocked off, all that weathering and erosion, not to mention the
graffiti and bird poop — who'd be a statue, eh.  There are chemical reactions afoot, which you
need to know a bit about.  That's what these questions are for — to keep you on your toes.

# Physical Weathering

Q1    Answer these questions about the properties of water.

a) When water freezes, does it expand or contract?

b) Explain what the words **expand** and **contract** mean.

Q2    Rainwater can seep into cracks in rock.

a) What will happen to the water if the temperature drops below 0°C?

b) How will this affect the cracks in the rock?

c) Draw a series of diagrams to show what will happen over a long period of time to the rock face below.  The temperature where it's situated is −10°C at night and 15°C during the day.

Q3    Describe conditions where bits of rock are most likely to break away from a rock face.

Q4    Some cliffs are made of great huge piles of rock fragments, called **scree**.

What does a huge sloping heap of scree tell you about what the **weather conditions** on the cliff were like in the past?

## This stuff cracks me up...

Freezing water (or 'ice' if you want to get technical) packs quite a punch.  Enough of a punch to break off hunks of mountain.  Learn how it works and remember it takes ages not just days.

# Effects of Weathering: Sediment

Q1   Put these pictures into the right sequence.

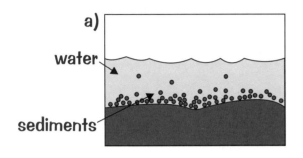

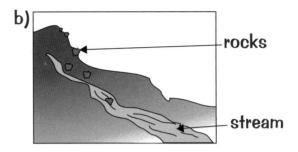

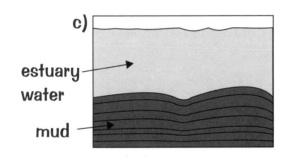

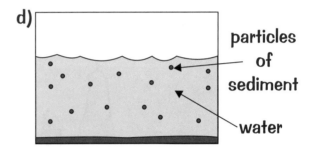

Q2   Think of bits of rock being carried along in a river.  Are bits of rock likely to be deposited where the water's moving quickly, or where it's moving slowly?

Q3   How do you think the size of sediment particle will affect the distance it can be carried along in a flowing river?

Q4   Look at the equipment in the grey box and then answer the questions below.

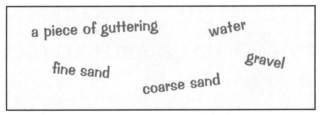

a) Using the equipment say how you would design an experiment to investigate your idea about sediment size and distance carried.

b) What variables are relevant to your experiment?

c) Which variables will you need to keep constant?

d) How would you keep each of those variables constant?

# *Effects of Weathering: Sediment*

**Q1** The table and the passage following it shows what happens if you shake cubes of plaster in a container.

| Number of Shakes | 0 | 5 | 10 | 15 | 20 |
|---|---|---|---|---|---|
| Number of Particles | 10 | 13 | 19 | 28 | 22 + dust |

The shape of the particles went from cubes at the beginning to much more like spheres at the end. After 10 shakes, there were a few little bits in the bottom of the container. After 20 shakes, there was quite a bit of dust at the bottom of the container.

a) Why do the bits of plaster get rounder?

b) Would you expect sediment grains in a river to get rounder and smaller as time went on? Explain your answer.

**Q2** After a big storm, the water in a river is at a higher level. The water also looks dirty and brown.

a) Why does the river look dirty?

b) When buildings get flooded, what gets left behind when the water level drops?

c) Which has a greater mass, 1 cubic metre of regular river water, or 1 cubic metre of flood water with a whole load of sediment in it?

**Q3** What are the fancy scientific names for these two things?

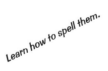
*Learn how to spell them.*

a) Particles of rock being carried along in water.

b) Deposited particles of rock that have settled out from the water.

## *Settle down you orrible specks of rock..*

Weathered rock produces sediment, which (as you'll find out later) becomes rock again, which gets shoved up into mountains, which get weathered producing sediment, which (as you'll probably know by now because you turned a couple of pages) becomes rock again, which gets... blah, blah, blah...

# _Sediment Layers_

**Q1**    Explain how layers of sedimentary rocks are formed deep under the sea.

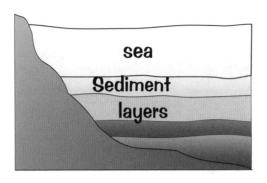

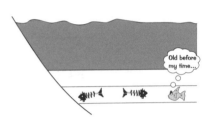

**Q2**    Read about the experiment, then answer the questions.

> _50 g of gravel was dropped into a beaker containing 200 ml of_
> _water.  The time taken for all the gravel to fall to the bottom was_
> _measured.  Then 50 g of coarse sand was dropped into a beaker_
> _containing 200 ml water.  The time taken for all the sand to fall_
> _to the bottom of the beaker was measured.  Lastly, the experiment_
> _was repeated with 50 g of very fine, black sand._

a) Which material do you expect to fall to the bottom of the beaker fastest?

b) If you poured the 50 g of very fine, black sand into a beaker containing water and coarse
   sand (that has already fallen to the bottom), you'd get two layers.  Would the border
   between the layers be sharp or blurry?

c) If you poured the 50 g of very fine black sand into the beaker of coarse sand and water
   **before** all the coarse sand had fallen to the bottom, you'd still get two layers.  This time,
   would the border between the layers be sharp or blurry?

**Q3**    Answer these questions about seawater.

a) Does seawater have salts dissolved in it?

b) If an inland sea starts to dry up, would the salt become more or less concentrated?

c) What will be left behind when all the water has evaporated?

**Q4**    Say what could eventually happen to the remains of a dead plant or animal that
   got covered with a layer of sediment, then another layer, then another layer...

# Sediment Layers

Q1 A layer of strata in sedimentary rock is made up of squashed sediment that was laid down over a period of time.

    a) Which are older — the layers above, or the layers below?

    b) If two fossils are found in the same layer, what can you say about their ages, relative to each other?

Q2 Match the images to the descriptions

| | |
|---|---|
| a) A river estuary, with mud particles being deposited. | 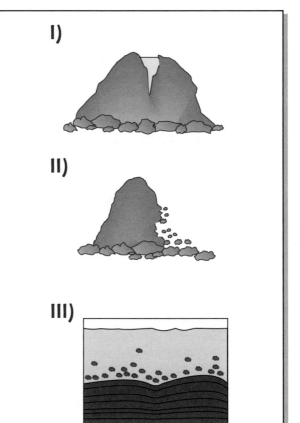 |
| b) A pile of scree | |
| c) cracks in rock that water can get into, freeze and expand | |

Q3 So, what did Mary Anning do at Lyme Regis that was so interesting?

You're supposed to find out about her, you see.
Write two paragraphs about her achievements.

*Research the answer using books, class notes, the internet etc.*

## He sediment to only stun it, but he took its head clean off...

... get shoved up into mountains, which get weathered producing sediment, which... Geeees this goes on a bit. Learn what sediment is, how it's formed, how it gets transported and how it settles out into layers and what it's all got to do with trilobites. (You know, the marine arthropod of Palaeozoic times, characterized by a three-lobed body.)

# Sedimentary Rock

Q1    What is sediment?

Q2    Name two sedimentary rocks.

Q3    Which of these statements are true of sedimentary rocks?

a) They are made up of grains of sediment.

b) They are non-porous.

c) They may contain fossils.

Q4    If you put a weight on top of some damp sand, what would you see?

Q5    Write a short paragraph to explain how sedimentary rock is formed.
Use some of the phrases below if you like.

"the layers of sediment are called strata"

"sediment is laid down over time"

"the pressure at the bottom of deep layers of strata is very high"

"the grains of sediment are squashed together"

Q6    Answer these questions about sedimentary rock.

a) What two things happen to sediment to turn it into sedimentary rock?

b) What's the "glue" that holds grains of sedimentary rocks together?

c) What is squeezed out from sediment as it gets compressed?

d) What might be left behind?

# Sedimentary Rock: Limestone

Q1    Do all limestones look exactly the same?

Q2    Read the information about limestones, and answer the questions.

> Limestones are mainly made of carbonates. Carbonates react with acids, producing carbon dioxide.

> You could compare the carbonate content of two limestones by seeing how much acid it takes to completely react with them.

a) How would you know whether the acid had completely reacted with all the carbonate?

b) How would you make sure that the acid reached all of the carbonate?

c) How would you make sure that you were making a fair comparison between the two limestone samples?

Q3    Look at the table, and answer the questions.

| Type of Limestone | Appearance | Carbonate Content |
|---|---|---|
| Portland stone (whitbed) | Smooth, with seashells in it | 92% |
| Chalk | Smooth but crumbly | 97% |
| Oolithic limestone | Lumpy, like lots of small balls | 85% |

a) Which limestone was probably made from sediment on the sea bottom that had been squashed a lot?

b) Which limestone was probably made by sediment fragments rolling around in thick mud and getting a bit of a coating?

c) These different limestones have different carbonate content. Does this mean that limestone is a compound, or a mixture?

## On the rocks with a twist of limestone...
Bet you never knew limestone could be that interesting.  OK, maybe not, but the point is this — you're supposed to be able to say how you'd do one of these comparisons.  Make sure you do.

# Metamorphic Rock

**Q1** Which of these are metamorphic rocks?

a) quartzite

b) granite

c) shale

d) slate

e) marble

f) chalk

**Q2** Look at these diagrams of samples of two rocks, and answer the questions about them below.

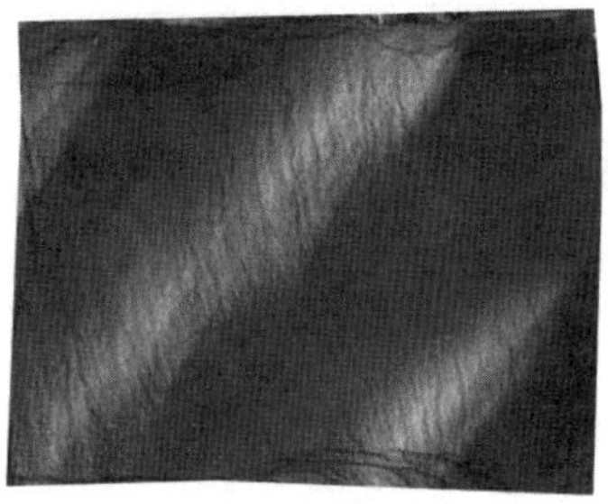

**Rock 1**

**Rock 2**

a) Which rock is more porous?

b) Which rock is harder?

**Q3** Write a paragraph describing how metamorphic slate is formed from sedimentary shale.

**Q4** What might happen to a fossil, when the sedimentary rock it was in, got heated and compressed and turned into metamorphic rock?

**Q5** Copy out the following paragragh filling in the gaps with words from the grey box.

.................... rocks are formed by the .................... of sediment layers. .................... rocks are formed from pre-existing rocks as a result of high .................... and / or high .................... .

| water content | sedimentary | pressure | temperature |
|---|---|---|---|
| erosion | metamorphic | altitude | big |

## My sister's a slate roof — it was the heat and pressure that did it...

What a lovely word — metamorphic... You need to be able to <u>spell</u> it, by the way, so if it gives you trouble, practise it. Same thing with these questions. Keep at 'em until you get them right.

# Igneous Rock

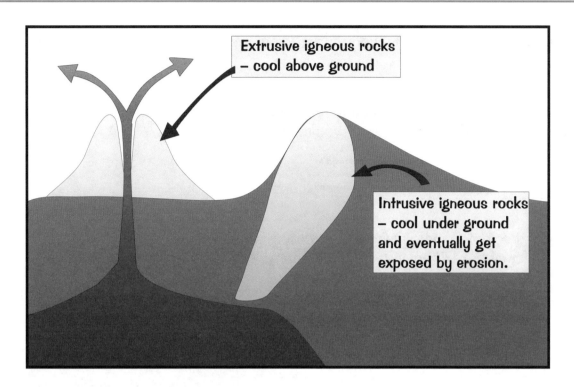

Extrusive igneous rocks – cool above ground

Intrusive igneous rocks – cool under ground and eventually get exposed by erosion.

**Q1** When a volcano erupts, lava flows out.
Where does this lava come from?

**Q2** Apart from red hot molten lava, what else can come out of a volcano during an eruption?

**Q3** When magma solidifies, it turns into igneous rock. Name three kinds of igneous rock.

**Q4** When magma cools slowly, **fewer** and **bigger** crystals are formed.
Why might this happen? Choose the best answer from the options below.

A Because the magma got hotter.

B Because the crystals have time to grow large before the rock completely solidifies.

C Because the magma was underground for longer.

**Q5** Explain the answer you picked for Q4 in terms of the particles in the crystals.

*Hint: crystals are formed when particles stick together in a regular pattern.*

## That volcano looks just like a great big, erupting zit...

Imagine that — rock melting like candlewax in the sun. Get it in your head that magma and lava are the same thing — molten rock — it's called magma when it's underground and lava when it's above ground. Then learn intrusive — cooled IN the ground, extrusive — cooled above ground.

# *Types of Igneous Rock*

**Q1** What evidence would you look for in a piece of rock to suggest that it was an igneous rock?

**Q2** Write down how would you find the relative densities of two pieces of rock.
(Remember that density = mass ÷ volume)

*Small hintette: you need to
explain how you'd measure
the mass and the volume*

**Q3** Copy and complete the sentences below using words
from the grey box.  Then answer the questions below.

*Hint:  You don't have to use all
of the words and you can use
words more than once.*

| dense | iron | | silica |
|-------|------|--------------|--------|
| steel | | sedimentary | igneous | fossils |

Gabbro is an .................... rock.  It's rich in ................... .   It's relatively dense.

Granite is an ................. rock.  It's mainly .................. . It isn't as ................. as gabbro.

Basalt is yet another ................. rock.  It's rich in ................... .

a) Which do you think is heavier, iron or silica?  Why?

b) Is basalt more like gabbro or granite?

**Q4** Explosive volcanic eruptions produce ash and pumice and not much lava flow.

a) Is pumice light or dense?  Describe the appearance of pumice.

b) Pumice stone is produced by explosive volcanoes (with violent and generally unpredictable eruptions).  Name one example of this type of volcano.

**Q5** Moderate volcanoes erupt often, and produce lots of streaming lava flow.

a) What igneous rock is produced by this sort of lava flow?

b) Name somewhere where this type of volcano can be found.

# The Rock Cycle

Q1 Look at the three descriptions of different types of rock, and match up each description with the right type of rock. Choose from the answers in the box.

a) "It's fairly smooth with small visible grains. You can see seashells in it. It's slightly porous"

b) "It's very smooth and dense, and dark grey. There are streaks in it"

c) "It's made of medium sized crystals in different shades of grey."

> sedimentary    metamorphic    igneous

Q2 How is **sedimentary** rock turned into **metamorphic** rock?

Q3 Rocks are **weathered** and **eroded** — by rain and the action of ice in cracks. What happens to the little bits of rock that get "weathered" off and washed away? What do we call the little bits of rock that get washed away in rivers and deposited?

Q4 Copy this diagram, and add labels. The labels you need are in the box below the diagram.

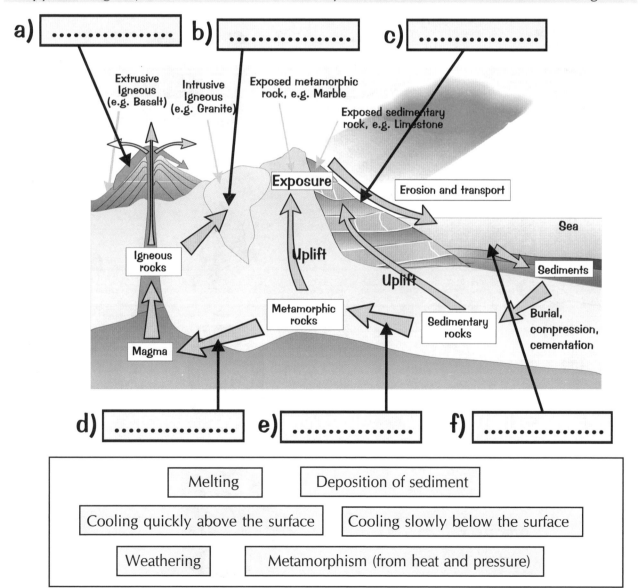

a) ..................
b) ..................
c) ..................
d) ..................
e) ..................
f) ..................

> Melting         Deposition of sediment
>
> Cooling quickly above the surface      Cooling slowly below the surface
>
> Weathering        Metamorphism (from heat and pressure)

# Temperature

**Q1**    What is temperature?

**Q2**    What are the units of temperature?

**Q3**    If a temperature is -18 °C, what does the minus sign mean?

**Q4**    Why do we have a temperature scale?

**Q5**    Suggest temperature values for the following:

An icy pond

Outside in winter

Inside a classroom

Outside in summer

Boiling water

Baker's oven

Body temperature

**Q6**    Match the correct thermometer to the correct use:

A

B

C

D

E

F

1    An ill person

2    ?

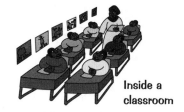
3    Inside an oven

4    Central heating boiler

5    Inside a fridge

6    Exothermic reaction

# *Temperature*

**Q1**   Which of the following are types of energy?

A) Light          D) Hot water

B) Heat          E) 55°C

C) Steam        F) 100 kJ in a chocolate bar

**Q2**   For heat to flow from one place to another there must be a temperature difference.
Draw out and label the diagram below with the following labels:

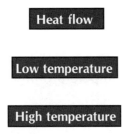

Heat flow

Low temperature

High temperature

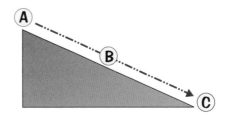

**Q3**   The diagram below shows a metal bar being heated at one end.
Copy the diagram and use the three labels to answer questions a) to c).

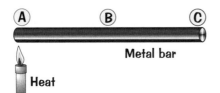

Room temperature

Above room temperature

Way above room temperature

What will the temperature be at positions A, B and C of the metal bar

a) before heating?

b) 5 seconds into heating?

c) after heating for 30 minutes?

**Q4**   Look at the diagram which shows a fuel burning and releasing energy.

a) What will happen to the temperature of the water as the fuels burns?

b) Explain how the energy in the fuel gets to the water.

c) Name the energy changes that occur when a
fuel burns like this and heats up some water.

d) If the fuel gave out more energy, what would happen
to the temperature reading on the thermometer?

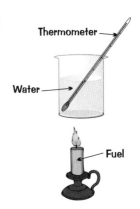

Thermometer

Water

Fuel

# *Conduction*

**Q1**   Which of the following would you find cold to the touch?

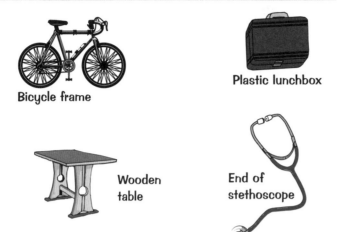

Bicycle frame

Plastic lunchbox

Wooden table

End of stethoscope

a) Under normal conditions, what would be the approximate temperature of
   i) the bike frame?     ii) the lunch box?     iii) your fingers?

b) For heat to flow there must be a temperature difference.
   Explain why certain objects feel cold and others feel warm.

c) Some materials are **good** at transferring heat from one place to another.
   What are these called?

d) Some materials are **not** good at transferring heat from one place to another.
   What are these called?

**Q2**   Classify the following as insulators or conductors.

   a) Copper                  d) Stainless steel

   b) Polythene               e) Aluminium

   c) Wood                    f)  Air

**Q3**   Copy and complete these sentences by choosing the correct words from the box.

   | insulators   metals   conductors   conductors |

   Most good thermal ................. are .................. .

   Poor thermal ................. are called .................. .

---

## *"I won't buy the duck, it's a rip off" — now that's con duck shun...*

This conduction malarkey can get quite confusing.  It'll help you loads if you remember some basic
facts like this:  Most <u>metals</u> are good heat conductors.  Most <u>non-metals</u> aren't — they're <u>insulators</u>.

---

# _Conduction_

Q1    Abby set up the apparatus below and heated the water at the top of the test tube. Very soon, the water at the top of the tube boiled.  However, the ice at the bottom of the tube did not melt.

a) Why did the water at the top boil?

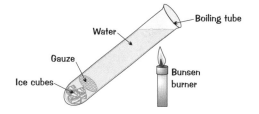

Good conductors of thermal (heat) energy transfer heat energy from one place to another quite quickly.

b) Explain why the ice cube at the bottom of the tube did not melt initially.

c) Abby continued to heat the water for about five minutes. What do you think happened?


Q2    And here's question two which is a lovely three-parter on conduction.  I hope you enjoy it.

a) Generally, which are the best conductors of thermal energy — solids, liquids or gases?

b) Which state of matter has particles closest together?

c) Is there a link between arrangement of particles and whether something is good at conducting?


Q3    Two teams of people are acting out how the particles in solids and liquids pass on their energy from one particle to another.

<u>First:</u>
Team A linked arms and an energetic boy at one end jiggled about trying to make his line move. This worked well and before long, the end person was moving

<u>Second:</u>
Team B held hands and an energetic boy at one end jiggled about trying to make his line move. This didn't work very well and no matter how the boy tried he couldn't get the end person to move very much at all.

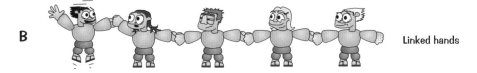

a) Which team were pretending to be a solid being heated at one end?

b) Which team were pretending to be a liquid being heated?

c) What was the energetic boy trying to simulate?

d) How does this model attempt to illustrate what happens when a solid and a liquid conduct thermal energy?

e) Another team, Team C, are going to enact how a gas might conduct heat energy. Suggest how team C might do this.

# *Expansion*

Q1    Draw diagrams to show what the particles look like in a gas, a liquid and a solid.

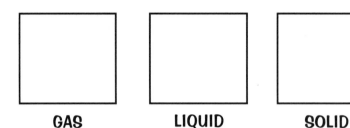

GAS          LIQUID          SOLID

Q2    The diagram below shows an experiment with a metal ball on a chain. Before heating, the ball fits through a ring. After the ball has been heated, it won't go through the ring. Explain what has happened.

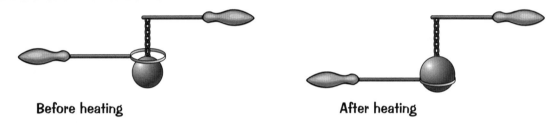

Before heating                    After heating

Q3    Look at the experiment below.

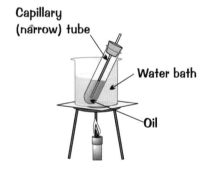

Capillary (narrow) tube

Water bath

Oil

a) Why does the oil travel up the capillary tube when it is put into the warm water bath?

b) What would you see if the test tube was removed from the water bath and the oil allowed to cool?

Q4    A round-bottomed flask full of air was warmed with warm hands and the tube coming out of it was placed into some water with red ink in it. After a few moments, bubbles could be seen coming from the capillary tube. The flask was clamped and allowed to return back to room temperature. Soon red liquid could be seen creeping up the capillary tube.

a) What state of matter is air?

b) Does warm air take up more or less volume than cold air?

c) Explain why bubbles could be seen coming from the flask as it was warmed

d) Explain why the red liquid crept up the tube as the flask cooled.

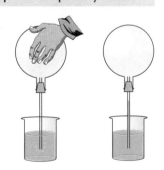

Q5    Draw out (using circles to represent the particles) what a solid might look like before heating and after heating (but not enough to melt it).

# Convection

Q1 A soluble coloured crystal was placed into cold water as shown below. The water was heated at one side of the beaker and a trail of colour could be seen as a convection current developed.

Choose the correct explanation to explain what has happened and copy it into your book.

* Warm water is more dense than cold so it rises causing a convection current.
* Warm water is less dense than cold so it rises causing a convection current.
* Warm water is more dense than cold so it sinks causing a convection current.
* Warm water is less dense than cold so it sinks causing a convection current.

Q2 Archie has filled his bath with really hot water. He adds lots of cold water and tests the temperature by sticking his toe into the top of the water, but it still feels too hot. Archie text messages a friend to tell him what has happened. His friend suggests the cold water has sunk to the bottom of the bath.

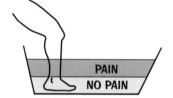

a) Explain why the cold water might have sunk to the bottom of the bath.

b) How could Archie tell if the cold water was at the bottom?

c) After a while Archie finds that the temperature of the water is now even throughout the bath. What has happened?

Q3 The beakers shown contain clear water and coloured water at various temperatures. Explain in as much detail as possible what has happened in case A and case B.

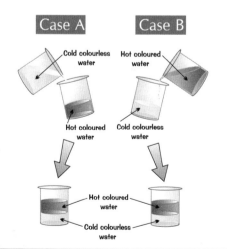

---

## The three states of matter — doesn't, no and of fact...

Convection is a bit of a weird one, but remember it's to do with density. Hotter things are <u>less dense</u> which makes them <u>lighter</u>. Convection is caused by hot air (or liquid) <u>rising</u>, and cool air (or liquid) <u>sinking</u>, creating a <u>current</u> where all the air (or liquid) gets heated. So 'air (or 'liquid) you go...

# _Radiation_

**Q1** Copy and complete the following paragraph using the words from the box.

| medium | radiation | energy | heat | convection | vacuum |
|---|---|---|---|---|---|

Conduction, ................. and ................. are ways by which ................. energy can be transferred from one place to another. Conduction and convection need a .............., which means that they need something to travel through. But radiation of ................. can occur through a ................. and does not require a medium.

**Q2** Copy each diagram and label it as **conduction**, **convection** or **radiation**.

a)

b)

c)

**Q3** Sarah is sitting in front of a log burner. Explain how she feels the heat of the fire.

**Q4** Dee heated each side of a metal plate with two Bunsen burners for an equal amount of time. One side was black and the other side was shiny. She then felt the heat radiating from each side.

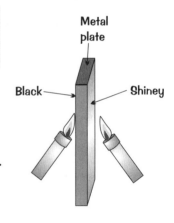

a) Which side of the plate would feel the hottest?

b) Which side is radiating heat the most?

c) Draw a diagram to show the heat being radiated from the plate.
(Use arrows to indicate radiation of heat energy.)

**Q5** Two teapot-making companies both make claims about their new and improved teapots. Which teapot do you think would be best at keeping the tea hot? Explain your answer.

**Q6** Is there a difference between thermal and radioactive radiation? Explain your answer.

# Reducing Heat Loss

Q1   List three ways a house may be insulated to stop heat loss.

Q2   Explain why homeowners are encouraged to insulate their homes

Q3   Explain how double glazing can help reduce heat loss.

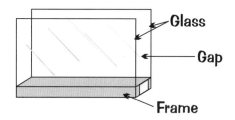

Q4   Modern houses have a cavity wall, which is an air gap between a double layer of brickwork. This is sometimes filled with a kind of foam which eventually sets hard.

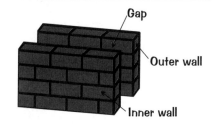

a) What is the purpose of the cavity in the wall?

b) Why do some homeowners fill the cavity with the foam?

Q5   Vacuum flasks are used to keep drinks hot, even in cold weather.

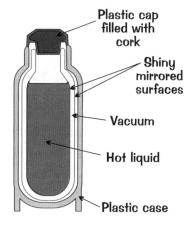

The words in bold are incorrect.  Copy the following sentences and correct the words in bold.

* The shiny surfaces of the vacuum flask **absorb** radiation back into the liquid
* The glass walls are **good** conductors of heat.
* The vacuum prevents the heat loss caused by **radiation** and convection.
* The top is made from plastic which is a good **conducting** material.

---

## *Flasks, picnics, sunshine, fresh air, pretty flowers, ah life is beautiful...*

Ah, a lovely page with some smashing examples of insulation.  It's all pretty easy to understand if you <u>learn</u> everything that's going on.  If you don't learn it, you'll get confused later on, I promise you.

# *Changing State*

Q1    Copy the diagram and complete the missing labels A, B, C, D.

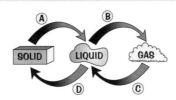

Q2    The melting point of sodium is 98 °C and that of oxygen is -219 °C.

a) Which has the highest melting point?

b) What temperature is the freezing point of sodium?

c) Why is it useful to know the boiling point of a substance?

Q3    A temperature probe linked to a data logger records the temperature of some
solid Salol (phenyl salicylate) as it is heated.  Graph 1 shows the results.

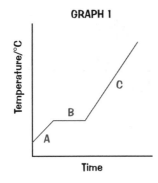

a) What's happening to the temperature in part A of the graph?

b) What's happening to the temperature in part B of the graph?

c) What's happening to the temperature in part C of the graph?

d) Copy out the sentences below, choosing the correct words
to explain what is happening in part B.

The Salol is being heated but the [temperature / weather] doesn't change.
The heat energy is being used to [weaken , strengthen] the bonds between
the [parsnips / particles] in the Salol to turn it into a [liquid / solid].

e) What would happen eventually if the substance continued to be heated?
(The answer has been jumbled up.  Write it out correctly.)

**hte ildiqu lolsa wluod ilob nad rnut toin a sga.**

Q4    Graph 2 shows the temperature of a substance
over time as it cools from a gas to a solid.
Describe what is happening in parts D to H.

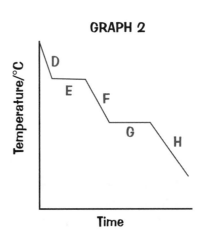

# Heating and Cooling — Review

**Q1**   Name the three states of matter.

**Q2**   Name all the changes in state which you have studied.

**Q3**   Name three ways by which heat can be transferred.

Boiling point is reached.

**Q4**   The boiling point of substance A is -100 °C.

a) Will substance A have a melting point above or below zero?

Substance B has a boiling point 13 °C less than substance A.

b) What is its boiling point?

Substance C has a boiling point 17 °C above that of substance A.

c) What is its boiling point?

**Q5**   Look at the picture below showing many different energy transfers. Copy and complete the labels by deciding if each one is **conduction**, **radiation** or **convection**.

Warm air rising causes ................. currents which create an onshore wind.

The air that lifts the balloon is heated by ...................

Sausages on barbeque grill are heated by .................. .................. and ..................

The sausage burns Johnny by ..................

Ice cream is melted by .................. from the sun.

Sunbathers are warmed by .................. from the sun.

Waves cool the sand by ..................

**Q6**   Loft insulation can be described as 'a blanket for the house'.
Explain what this means and explain how loft insulation and a blanket are similar.

## The last page of a WONDERFUL section — don't worry, it's OK to cry...

Question 5 up there is a good one for checking you understand the 3 heat transfers.  If it doesn't seem really obvious, you need to do some more learning.  I'm off to watch Hollyoaks now.  See ya.

# Magnets

**Q1** Copy out this table and put a tick in the box you think is correct for each object.

| Object | Attracted by magnet | Not attracted by magnet |
|---|---|---|
| Plastic cup | | |
| Nickel coin | | |
| Iron nail | | |
| Aluminium can | | |
| Paper | | |
| Lead soldier | | |
| Wooden ruler | | |
| Steel knife | | |
| Gold coin | | |
| Polythene bag | | |

**Q2** Write out a list of the metals that are attracted by a magnet.
One is missing from the table in question 1. Which one is this?

**Q3** Magnets are useful around the house. Say how they are useful in:

a) a fridge

b) a wardrobe

c) a screwdriver

d) an electric can opener

e) a loudspeaker

**Q4** You're given three pieces of steel, labelled A, B and C. They all look the same, but two are magnets and one is not. One end of each piece of steel is labelled with an X. You get these results from an experiment:

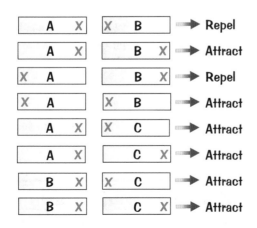

| | | |
|---|---|---|
| A X | X B | → Repel |
| A X | B X | → Attract |
| X A | B X | → Repel |
| X A | X B | → Attract |
| A X | X C | → Attract |
| A X | C X | → Attract |
| B X | X C | → Attract |
| B X | C X | → Attract |

*Remember that attract means pull together and repel means push apart.*

Copy these sentences out using the correct words.

a) The piece of steel labelled A [is / is not] a magnet.

b) The piece of steel labelled B [is / is not] a magnet.

c) The piece of steel labelled C [is / is not] a magnet.

d) Only two magnets can [attract / repel] each other.

# Magnets

Q1 A fridge magnet holds an important note to the door of the fridge.
Copy out the following sentences using the correct words.

a) Paper [is / is not] magnetic.

b) The fridge door [is / is not] magnetic.

c) Magnetism [does / does not] act through paper.

Q2 Rivaldo is testing different materials to see if magnetism
will act through them. The diagram shows the experiment.

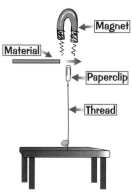

a) Write down what will happen to the
paper clip when the sheet of material is:

i)   Cardboard          iii) Steel          v)   Iron

ii)  Aluminium          iv) Copper          vi)  Tin

b) Write down the materials which allow magnetism to act through them.

c) Write down the materials which act as a shield to magnetism.

d) What is special about the materials which act as a shield to magnetism?

Q3 Ronaldo is given an iron nail which is not yet a magnet. He is told to make the
iron nail into a magnet. He is also given a steel bar magnet to help him do this.

a) Draw a diagram to show how he would make the iron nail into a magnet.
Don't forget to label the diagram.

b) Draw another diagram to show how he could test the iron nail
and show that it had become a magnet.

c) Write down a sentence to explain how he could destroy the magnetism of the iron nail.

Q4 Ronaldinho is asked to test two magnets to see which is stronger.
He decides to hang paper clips on the end of each magnet.
The first magnet holds 4 paper clips. The second magnet holds 8 paper clips.

a) Which magnet is stronger, the first or the second?

b) Say how much stronger the magnet is.

---

## Chat up line #25 — we go together like opposite poles of bar magnets...

A lot of people think that all metals are attracted to
magnets. **THEY'RE NOT.** It's just these ones, see:

Other metals

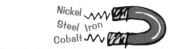

Nickel
Steel  Iron
Cobalt

---

# *Magnetic Fields*

Q1    A steel bar magnet is hung on a cradle by a thread.
The magnet is allowed to swing freely.

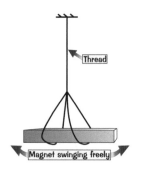

a) What will have happened to the magnet
   when it eventually stops moving?

b) Hill walkers use a compass and a map to find their way.
   What is the needle of the compass made of?

c) How is the compass needle suspended so that it can swing freely?

d) What is the end of a magnet that points to the North pole of the earth called?

e) What is the end of a magnet that points to the South pole of the earth called?

f) Copy out these sentences using the correct words.

   i)   At the North pole of the earth there must be a magnetic [north / south] pole.

   ii)  At the South pole of the earth there must be a magnetic [north / south] pole.

   iii) The north pole of a magnet is always attracted by the [north / south] pole of another magnet.

   iv)  The south pole of a magnet is always repelled by the [north / south] pole of another magnet.


Q2    Copy out the diagram to the right which shows
the shape of the magnetic field around a magnet.

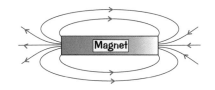

a) On the diagram:

   i) Draw an N to show the position of the magnetic north pole.

   ii) Draw an S to show the position of the magnetic south pole.

   iii) Mark with an X somewhere where the magnetic field is strong.

   iv) Mark with a Y somewhere where the magnetic field is weak.

b) Copy these sentences using the correct words.

   i)   Around a bar magnet the magnetic field always goes from
        the magnetic [north / south] pole to the magnetic [north / south] pole.

   ii)  The closer you are to a pole of a magnet, the [stronger / weaker] the magnetic field.

   iii) The further you are away from the pole of a magnet, the [stronger / weaker] the magnetic field.

   iv)  The shape of the magnetic field around a bar magnet can be shown
        using [iron filings / wood chippings] sprinkled near to the magnet.

   v)   A compass always lines up [along / across] the magnetic field lines.

# Magnetic Fields

Q1    A small compass is used to show the direction of a magnetic field. The compass needle points in the direction of the magnetic field. An example is shown in the diagram to the right.

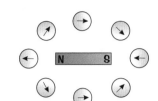

Copy the diagrams below. Draw in each circle an arrow to show the direction in which the compass needle is pointing.

a)

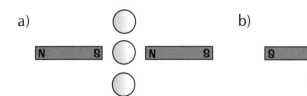

b)

c)

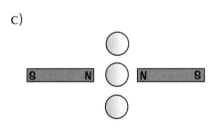

Q2    At a really exciting birthday party, Charley and his friends make an electromagnet by wrapping some insulated copper wire around a large iron nail. They then connect the electromagnet into an electric circuit as shown in the diagram.

a) They decide to test the strength of the electromagnet.

    i) How could they change the size of the electric current in the circuit?

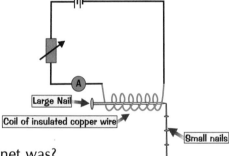

    ii) How could they measure the size of the electric current in the circuit?

    iii) How could they decide how strong the electromagnet was?

    iv) How could they make the electromagnet pick up more small nails?

b) Write down what you think would happen to the small iron nails if:

    i) more turns of insulated copper wire are wrapped on the large iron nail.

    ii) the iron nail is replaced by a piece of wood of the same size.

    iii) a piece of nickel is used instead of the large iron nail.

## _Charley and his mates — they know how to have a good time..._

What, you don't see the ATTRACTION of magnets? You find them REPELsive? What about that Tango advert where the man wearing a deep sea diving suit filled with oranges gets picked up by a big magnet and dropped... That was great, wasn't it? You like them now, don't you...

# _Electromagnets_

Q1    An electromagnet is used to make an electric bell work.
      Copy out the following sentences using the correct words.

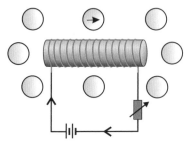

When the switch is closed a [magnetic / electric] current
flows through the wires.  The core of the electromagnet
is made into a [temporary / permanent] magnet.  The electromagnet
[repels / attracts] the springy steel connected to the hammer, which strikes the gong.
The contacts are now [opened / closed] and the electric current stops flowing.
The core of the electromagnet now [stops / starts] being a magnet.  The springy steel moves
[away from / towards] the gong.  The contacts are now [closed / opened] and the electric
current flows again.  The whole process [starts / stops] again.

Q2    A relay is an electromagnetic switch.  It uses a small current from an
      input circuit to switch a large current in an output circuit on and off.

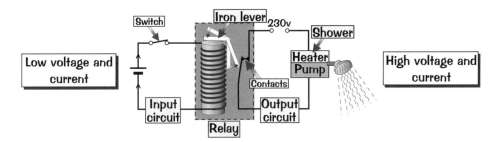

a) The switch in the input circuit is closed.  What happens to the current in the input circuit?

b) The iron lever on the top of the electromagnet is pulled down.  Explain why this happens.

c) The iron lever pushes the contacts in the output circuit together.
   What happens in the output circuit?

d) The switch in the input circuit is now opened.
   Describe carefully what happens as a result of this.

Q3    A small compass is placed at different positions around an electromagnet.

a) Copy the diagram and show the direction of
   the compass needle at each position.
   One of the directions has been done for you.

b) What would happen to the directions
   if the electric current was reversed?

c) The current is changed back to its original direction and
   the iron core is removed.  What do you think will happen to the compass needles?

d) The current is switched off.  What will happen to all the compass needles now?

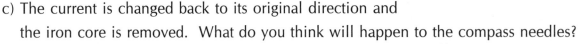

## How Light Travels

Q1    Which of these are light sources?

         A:   a star        D:   the Moon

         B:   a mirror      E:   white paper

         C:   a laser       F:   a candle

Q2    The sentences below are in the wrong order.
Write them out in the correct order.

     A:   This is because light travels much more quickly than sound.

     B:   Some time later you hear the thunder.

     C:   Lightning strikes a distant hill.

     D:   You see the lightning first.

Q3    Light travels very quickly but it still takes time to travel. Copy out this chart and the distances. Then fill in the time column putting the times in their correct order.

| Distance travelled by light | Time taken |
| --- | --- |
| across a room | eight minutes |
| to the moon | almost instantly |
| from the sun | just over a second |
| from a different star | many years |

Q4    Write "true" or "false" for each of these statements.

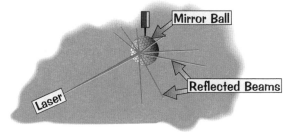

a) The mirror ball makes its own light.

b) The smoke shows you the path of the laser beam.

c) The laser could change direction in mid air.

d) The laser travels in a straight line until it hits the mirror ball.

e) The laser only changes direction at the mirror.

f) The reflected laser beams are strong enough to blind a dancer.

## Thunder, lightning and lasers — not a bad start to the section...

Don't get light <u>sources</u> mixed up with things that just <u>reflect</u> light. Sure, the Moon shines happily down at you every night, but what you're <u>really</u> seeing is light from the Sun <u>reflected</u> off the Moon.

# *When Light Meets an Object*   the full, juicy story...

**Q1**    Copy out each sentence and complete it using the correct keyword.

| transparent    translucent    opaque    absorb    reflect    transmit |

a)  A mirror will ................. light that lands on it.

b)  An ................. material will stop light altogether.

c)  Black paint will ................. almost all the light that lands on it.

d)  A ................. material will allow light to pass through really easily.

e)  A ................. material will allow light through but scatters it about
so that you can't see anything.

f)  A dirty mirror will ................. some light but it will also
................. some, making your face look dull.

g)  The windows in a car are ................. so that they ................. light.

**Q2**    This table is a real mess.  Copy it out, putting the materials into the correct columns.

| Transparent | Translucent | Opaque |
|-------------|-------------|--------|
| brick | wood | glass |
| cloud | water | fog |
| air | steel | Outer Space |
| lead | tracing paper | scratched glass |

**Q3**    Say which of these statements are true and which are false.

A:  Luminous objects need a light source to be seen.

B:  The Moon makes its own light.

C:  Dark objects reflect less light than bright ones.

D:  Light goes out of your eye so that you can see things.

E:  In daylight the Sun is the original source of the light that you see things with.

F:  A ray is the name given to the path that light follows.

**Q4**    Use the idea that light travels in straight lines to explain why:

a)  The mechanic can't shine a light on the bottom of the engine just using the torch.

b)  The mirror lights up the bottom of the engine.

c)  The mechanic can now see the bottom of the engine.

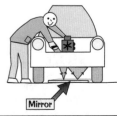

Mirror

# How Mirrors Work

**Q1** Match the keyword up with its correct description.

a) The picture that you see in a mirror.

b) Turned upside down or from side to side or both.

c) A plastic semicircle used to measure angles.

d) The ray that goes into the mirror.

e) A device, containing two mirrors, which is used in submarines.

f) The science word for a flat surface.

g) A device, containing two or more mirrors, which can be used to make patterns.

h) A line drawn at an angle of ninety degrees to a mirror.

i) The ray that reflects away from a mirror.

j) An illusion created using the image in a flat sheet of glass.

> inverted    plane
> protractor    reflected ray
> periscope    Pepper's ghost
> kaleidoscope
> normal    image    incident ray

**Q2** Complete these sentences. The keywords from Q1 should give you some hints...

When light .............. from a mirror you should measure all .............. with respect to the .............. . The angle that the light ray goes in at is called the angle of .............. . This is equal to the .............. of .............. . The .............. in a mirror is .............. from side to side but not from top to bottom. This means that it is the right way up but the wrong way round.

**Q3** Copy out and complete these ray diagrams.

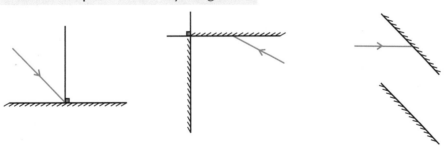

**Q4** Quiz questions. All of these situations require you to think about mirrors.

a) Which capital letters look the same in the mirror? *(e.g. A and O do but K doesn't)*

b) Why does an ambulance have mirror-writing on the front?

c) Why does the fact that a periscope has two mirrors make what you see through it easier to understand?

---

## _Mirror mirror on the wall — who's the boredest of us all..._

That's why you always look different on photographs from how you look in the mirror.
Your face isn't perfectly symmetrical, so when you look at yourself in the mirror, you don't
see what everyone else sees — just some kinda backwards version of yourself. Yup.

# The Spectrum and Bending Light

**Q1** For each of these situations, say whether it's caused by **reflection** or **refraction**.

a) A swimming pool looks to be shallower than it really is.

b) You get that nasty glare shining up from a wet road in the sun.

c) A pencil looks bent when you stick it into some water.

*Reflection = light bounces off things. Refraction = light goes through but might bend on the way in or out.*

d) You can see the Moon.

f) Your legs look short and fat in a river.

e) Stars twinkle.

g) A prism splits white light into colours.

**Q2** Copy and complete these diagrams where light is being shone onto glass blocks:

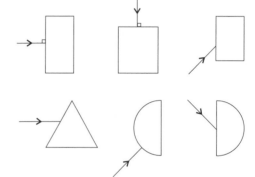

**Q3** Solve these anagrams.
(The answers are all to do with the spectrum.)

a) der

b) lube

c) enger

d) i dingo

e) to vile

f) go near

g) yo well

h) ow brian!

i) simpr

j) cures pmt

k) so inspired

**Q4** The answers to these questions are all colours or lists of colours.

a) Name the colours of the rainbow (the spectrum).

b) Isaac Newton listed seven colours in the spectrum. Which colour is the one that most people can't make out as a separate colour?

c) What colour would you see if you used a second prism to recombine the spectrum made by a prism?

d) A TV remote set uses light that your eyes can't quite see. Which colour that you <u>can</u> see is it closest to?

e) What's your favourite colour?

f) Which colour is bent most by a prism?

g) Which colour does a prism bend least?

*Remember this old cookie:*
*<u>R</u>ichard <u>O</u>f <u>Y</u>ork <u>G</u>ave <u>B</u>attle <u>I</u>n <u>V</u>ain*

*Ahh that's just beautiful to watch...*

*...the mouse has used the old prism defence to perfection.*

---

## Shut that door — our mam's been refracting kippers again...

The rainbow — one of nature's little wonders... OK, so it's rainy, yeah — loads of <u>water</u> in the air. Sun comes out. <u>Sunlight</u> travels through the <u>atmosphere</u>, hits the <u>water</u> and <u>bends</u> the light. <u>Each colour</u> of light is bent by a <u>different amount</u>. <u>White</u> light <u>splits</u> beautifully into a rainbow.

# _Colours_

Q1   Identify which of these statements are **true** and which are **false**.

a)   The spectrum contains seven colours.

b)   The primary colours (**in science**) are red, green and blue.

c)   The only colour that cannot be made from the primary colours is white.

d)   White surfaces reflect all colours equally well.

e)   Computer monitor screens are covered in very small rainbow-coloured dots.

f)   Yellow can be made by adding red and blue light together.

g)   A filter absorbs the colours that it doesn't transmit.

h)   A coloured surface absorbs the colours that you see and reflects the ones that you don't.

Use this summary chart to answer questions 2 and 3.

| Colour of surface or filter (Colour seen in eye) | Colours of light absorbed | Light reflected, transmitted or needed to see this colour |
|---|---|---|
| red | green and blue | red |
| blue | red and green | blue |
| green | red and blue | green |
| cyan | red | blue and green |
| magenta | green | blue and red |
| yellow | blue | red and green |
| black | all (red, green and blue) | none |
| white | none | all (red, green and blue) |
| other colour | mixture of red, green and blue | mixture of red, green and blue |

Q2   Complete the following statements.

a)   If white light shines on a red filter, ........... and ........... are absorbed but ........... is transmitted.

b)   If white light shines on a yellow surface ........... is absorbed but ........... and ........... are reflected.

c)   If blue light shines on a yellow filter ........... light is transmitted.

d)   If a coloured pencil reflects red and blue light then you would see the colour ........... .

e)   If yellow light shines on a green surface then ........... is reflected.

f)   If ........... , ........... and ........... are absorbed completely then you see ........... .

Q3   Copy out and complete these diagrams.

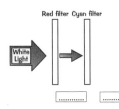    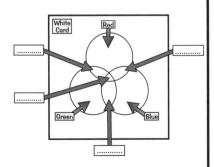

# Pitch and Loudness

Q1　Copy out these sentences and fill in the blanks.　Use the words in the grey box.

*Hint: You can use words more than once.*

| quiet | high | low | loud | vibrating | pitch | volume |
|---|---|---|---|---|---|---|

a) Sounds are produced when objects are .................. .

b) The .................. of the sound from a bass guitar is usually .................. .

c) The .................. of the sound from a whistle is usually .................. .

d) A jet engine is ................. because its .................. is high.

e) A whisper is .................. because its .................. is low.

Q2　A guitar can make different musical notes.　The sentences below the diagram are muddled up. Match the start of each sentence with the correct ending and then copy them all out.

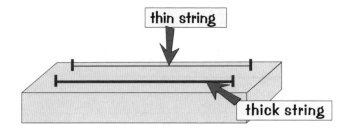

thin string

thick string

a) Using a thicker string...　　　gives a higher note.

b) Tightening the string...　　　gives a louder note.

c) Making the string shorter...　　　gives a lower note.

d) Making a bigger vibration...　　　gives a higher note.

Q3　Ahmed is at a disco.　He is listening to the music and he decides to move closer to the speakers.

a) Describe what a speaker is doing to produce a sound.

b) As he moves towards the speaker, describe:

　i)　how the **loudness** of the sound Ahmed hears changes.

　ii)　what happens to the pitch of the sound.

Ahmed

loudspeaker

## Pop music these days — it's just all pitch and volume...

Musical instruments let you change the <u>pitch</u> (e.g. by changing the length of the strings) and <u>volume</u> (e.g. by hitting/plucking/blowing harder or softer).　And that's how you make music, sweet sweet music...

# *Sound Waves*

**Q1** Copy these sentences, filling in the blanks.

The l................... of a sound is how loud or quiet it seems to us.  It is decided by the

a................... , which is the size of the v................... .  The p................... of a sound is how

high or low it seems to us.  It is decided by the f................... , which is how fast the object

v................... .

**Q2** Read this passage, look at the oscilloscope pictures and then answer the questions below.

Emily has been studying bees.  She has found out that their wings beating the air as they fly cause a buzzing sound.

She used a microphone and oscilloscope to show the pattern of the sound from four species of bee (A, B, C and D).  These oscilloscope pictures show her results: *(She didn't change any settings on the oscilloscope.)*

a) Which of the bees has

   i)  the quietest buzz?

   ii)  the lowest frequency buzz?

   iii)  the loudest buzz?

b) Which two bees are beating their wings at the same frequency?

**Q3** Here are five different musical instruments.

 guitar      trombone      triangle     violin      drum

For each instrument:

a) Say what you have to do to get a musical sound out of it.
   *(Note:  there could be more than one way for some of these instruments.)*

b) Say what vibrates to make the sound.

c) Say how you can make the sound louder.

d) Say how you can make the pitch higher.
   *(Note:  there could be more than one way for some of these instruments.)*

# The Speed of Sound

**Q1**  Jermaine watched a storm from his house.  Using his watch, he discovered that the gap between seeing the lightning and hearing the thunder was 6 seconds.

a) Why is there a gap between seeing the lightning and hearing the thunder?

b) Describe how the sound travels through the air to get to Jermaine.

c) Jermaine's science teacher told him that sound travels about one kilometre in three seconds.  How far away from Jermaine's house was the lightning strike?

**Q2**  Here is a diagram of the famous bell jar experiment:

a) Describe what you would notice as the pump takes the air out of the jar.

b) How could you be sure the clock was still ringing?

c) What (apart from the clock and the foam) is inside the jar

   i)  at the start?     ii)  at the end?

d) Why is the clock sitting on a foam block rather than resting on the jar base?

e) What can you conclude from this experiment?

**Q3**  Kylie and her friends wanted to measure the speed of sound in air.  They start the stopwatch as soon as they see the flash of the gun and stop it when they hear the sound.  Use Kylie's figures to work out the speed of sound they measured.

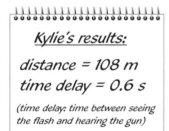

_Kylie's results:_

distance = 108 m
time delay = 0.6 s

(time delay: time between seeing the flash and hearing the gun)

measured distance

**Q4**  Sound travels faster through some substances than others.  Here are some examples.

| Substance | air | water | concrete | steel |
|---|---|---|---|---|
| Speed of sound (m/s) | 340 | 1500 | 4000 | 5000 |

a) Show these figures on a bar chart.

b) Copy these sentences and fill in the blanks, using the words **solids**, **liquids** or **gases**:

Sound travels fastest through ................. and slowest through ................. .
Sound travels faster through ................. like water than through ................. .

# Hearing

**Q1** The diagram shows Pooja and George using a string telephone.

a) Explain how the string telephone works.

b) Why does the string have to be stretched?

c) When Pooja and George stretch the string round a corner they find it doesn't work. Explain why not.

d) They decide the telephone would work better with a steel wire instead of string. How could they do a fair test to find out if they are right?

**Q2** Your friend, who is good at science and knows all about the particle model, was away when you learnt about how sound travels. Write a few clear notes to explain what you know. You can draw some neat diagrams to help make things clear.

**Q3** Different animals can hear different ranges of sound pitch. This is called their audible range. The bar chart shows the audible range for some animals.

a) Which of these animals...

   i) ...can hear sounds higher than humans?

   ii) ...have a smaller audible range than humans?

b) What is the name we give to sounds which are too high for humans to hear?

c) What do bats use high-pitched sound for?

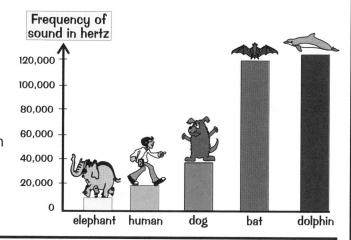

---

## I wish they'd put Gareth Gates in a vacuum...

So just remember, sound needs a medium — it can't travel through <u>vacuums</u>, it travels faster through <u>denser</u> materials, it travels much <u>slower than light</u> and different animals can hear different <u>pitch ranges</u>. Phew! And I bet you thought you were in for an easy ride after page 78...

# _Hearing_

Q1    The diagram shows the structure of a human ear.

a) Write down the
   names and functions
   of the parts labelled
   1 to 5. Choose the
   functions from
   these phrases:

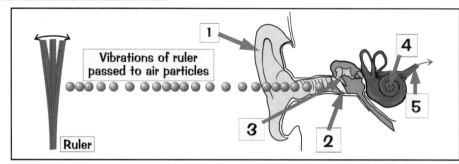

Vibrations of ruler
passed to air particles

Ruler

- Passes the sound along the middle ear.
- Vibrates when sound hits it.
- Collects sound and funnels them down the ear canal.
- Sends electrical signals to brain.
- Translates sound into electrical signals.

b) When we hear things there is a complicated series of things happening.
   Here are the six main stages in a jumble. Write them out in the right order.

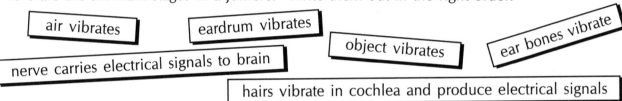

air vibrates

eardrum vibrates

object vibrates

ear bones vibrate

nerve carries electrical signals to brain

hairs vibrate in cochlea and produce electrical signals

Q2    Henry and Janine want to compare the audible range of
      different people. They have been given this equipment.

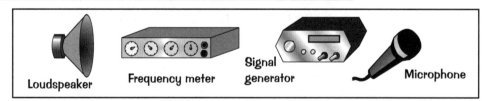

Loudspeaker    Frequency meter    Signal generator    Microphone

a) What is the job of: i) the signal generator? ii) the loudspeaker? iii) the frequency meter?

b) What should they keep the same for each person if they wanted to make a fair comparison
   of the audible range?

Q3    Joanne says that rabbits have big ears so they can hear very soft sounds.

a) Why would that be useful for a rabbit?

b) Joanne decides to do an investigation. She can't tell a rabbit what to do, so she has to fit
   cardboard ears on her friend Henry. How could she do a fair investigation to see if large
   ears really do help to hear softer sounds?

---

### _My friend Dom is a loudspeaker — I just wish he could TALK A BIT QUIETER!!!_

Cardboard rabbit ears? This is getting far too silly. And what on earth is going on at the top of the
page? Stop flicking peas into that man's ear! No, I won't stand for any of this... I'm off.

---

# *Investigating Sound*

**Q1**   The diagram shows the intensity of some sounds.

a) What word does dB stand for?

b) People working in noisy places have
to wear 'ear defenders' to cut down
the sound intensity getting in their
ears.  Explain why this is important.

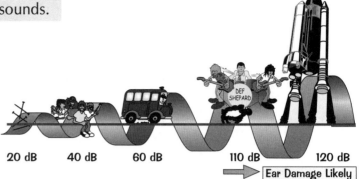

20 dB     40 dB     60 dB        110 dB      120 dB

➡ Ear Damage Likely

**Q2**   Dhanesh and Judith are investigating how the pitch of a sound
produced by a stretched string depends on how long it is.

a) What factors do they have to keep the same if it is to be a fair test?

b) They get these results:

| Length of string (cm) | 10 | 20 | 30 | 40 | 50 |
|---|---|---|---|---|---|
| Pitch of sound (Hz) | 500 | 250 | 168 | 125 | 100 |

   i)  What is Hz short for?    ii)  Draw a graph to show these results.

c) Use your graph to answer these questions.

   i) What would be the pitch of the sound if the string was 15 cm long?

   ii)  How long would the string be if the sound had a pitch of 200 Hz?

d) Here is Judith's conclusion.  Copy out and finish her sentences:

| The longer the string the... | | If we halve the length of the string the pitch... |
|---|---|---|

**Q3**   Sailors can use sound waves to measure how deep
the sea is.  The diagram shows how it's done.

The boat sends out a loud PING! which hits
the sea bottom and comes back.  Equipment
on board picks up the returning (now
quieter) ping and times how long it took to
come back.  The sailors know that sound
travels at 1500 metres per second in water.

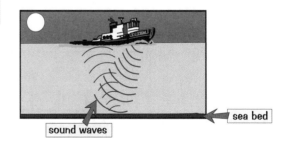

sound waves     sea bed

a) What do we call the sound that hits the seabed and comes back?

b) The sound takes 3 seconds to get back to the boat.

*HINT: if you know how long it took to get
to the seabed, and you know how far it
travels in one second ... get the idea?*

   i)  How long did it take to get to the seabed?

   ii)  How long did it take to get back to the boat from the seabed?

   iii)  Using the information you have got work out how deep the sea must be at this place.

# Investigating Sound

Q1  Jack and Jill want to find out how good sound insulation is.

Here is a diagram of their equipment:

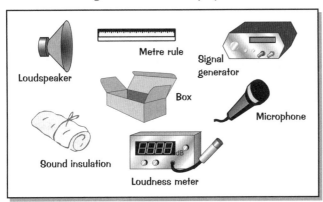

This is what they thought might happen:

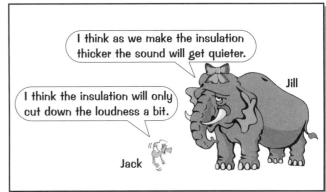

Answer these questions to describe how they could do a fair test on the insulating material.

a) How would you arrange the equipment? (HINT: Draw a diagram to help.)

b) What measurements would they make?

c) How would they make sure it was the insulation that made any difference and not something else? (HINT: where would they put the loudness meter?)

Q2  Copy out this puzzle. Solve the clues and write the letters in the correct spaces.

i)   Sound can't travel through this.
ii)  The part of the ear that vibrates first when sound reaches it.
iii) The _ _ _ _ _ of sound in air is about 330 metres per second.
iv)  Use this to make sound quieter.
v)   Loud noises can damage your hearing. This is one problem, also called 'ringing in the ears'.
vi)  Everything that makes a sound does this.
vii) How many vibrations every second, measured in hertz. It decides the pitch of a sound.
viii) How big the vibrations are decide this for a sound.
ix)  This is the unit we use to measure viii).

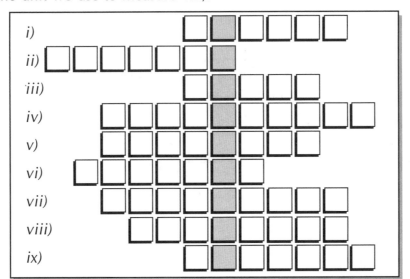

When you have finished, the shaded boxes should give you the word meaning 'the biggest distance a particle moves in a wave, which decides how loud a sound is'.

# The Answers

## Unit 8A — Food and Digestion

### Page 1

Q1 A cow eats grass.
A snail eats algae.
A spider eats flies.
A green plant makes its own food.
A human eats meat and vegetables.

Q2 Playing tennis.

Q3 The food in your breakfast provides the energy you need to be active until lunch.

Q4 growth

Q5 Food is needed to make new cells to repair tissue.

Q6 • All living things need energy.
• Food is the raw material for growth and repair. • Food provides the energy needed for movement.

### Page 2

Q1

Q2 a) Carbohydrate
b) More protein
c) 9.0g of fibre
d) Sodium and iron
e) 3 kinds of vitamins

Q3 a) Yellow or brown
b) Blue/black
c) Starch (a carbohydrate)

Q4 a) Yes, glucose was present.
b) Eye protection.

Q5 Cut the food into small pieces and add it to a small amount of alcohol. Shake the test tube then add cold water. If it goes cloudy white, fat is present.

Q6
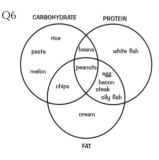

### Page 3

Q1 a) Bread is a good source of carbohydrate.
b) Good sources of protein are fish and meat.
c) Margarine is a good source of fat.
d) Celery and wholemeal bread contain fibre.
e) Oranges contain a lot of vitamin C.
f) Milk is a good source of calcium.

Q2 a)
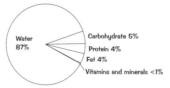

b) % Protein in different foods

c) Nutrients in soya beans and broad beans
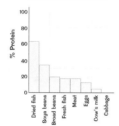

Q3 Fat provides energy.
Carbohydrate provides energy.
Protein is used for growth and repair.
Fibre prevents constipation.
Vitamins and minerals in small quantities are necessary for good health.

Q4 a) Protein provides the raw materials for building new muscle and bone so without it the child does not grow.
b) Eggs contain more protein than bread. Protein is needed to make muscle.
c) Rice and pasta contain a lot of carbohydrate. Carbohydrate provides energy for movement.

### Page 4

Q1 A balanced diet contains carbohydrate, fat, proteins, vitamins, minerals, fibre and water in the correct amounts.

Q2 True:
• Eating too much carbohydrate can make you fat.
• "Organic" foods are produced without manufactured fertilisers, pesticides or weedkillers.
• Green vegetables are good for you.
• Pregnant women need more minerals in their diet.
• Eating vegetable oils rather than animal fats will reduce the chance of heart disease.
• Eating fruit and vegetables can help to prevent constipation.
• Many years ago sailors on long sea journeys ate limes to prevent a disease called scurvy.

False:
• Eating crusts makes your hair curly.
• The more vitamins you eat the healthier you will be.
• Cancer of the bowel is caused by not eating enough fibre.

Possibly true:
• "Organic" foods are better for you than ordinary foods.

Q3 Many human volunteers took the supplement and they were examined by doctors every month for two years.
The health of the volunteers was compared with that of a matched group of people who did not take the supplement.
The original research work on the supplement was published in a well known scientific journal.

# The Answers

## Page 5

Q1 Quiz questions and answers:
- Why do we need food?
  — To provide raw materials and for energy
- Give three uses of energy in the body.
  — Growth, repair and movement
- In the biuret test, what colour shows that protein is present? — Violet or blue
- When testing for sugar, what must you do after adding Benedict's reagent?
  — Heat it
- Name the reagent used to test for starch.
  — Iodine solution
- What does a balanced diet contain?
  — The right amount of each nutrient
- Give three good sources of protein.
  — Meat, fish and beans
- Bread and rice are good sources of this.
  — Carbohydrate
- Small amounts of these are present in foods. — Vitamins and minerals
- Nuts are a good source of which nutrients? — Carbohydrate, protein and fat.
- Liver is a good source of which mineral?
  — Iron
- For which two processes is protein needed?  — Growth and repair.
- Which two nutrients provide energy?
  — Carbohydrates and fat
- Which provides more energy per gram, carbohydrate or fat? Fat.
- These are a good source of protein for vegetarians. — Beans
- Herbivores can digest this but we can not. — Fibre
- Humans can only live a few days without this. — Water
- Processed foods often contain too much of this mineral. — Sodium

Q2 Any two of these:
The woman might not be telling the truth.
A lot more people would have to test out the chocolate diet.
She may be healthy now but may suffer in the long term.
The "chocolate" she has been eating may have been specially manufactured to contain all the nutrients in the right proportions.
(or any other sensible answer)

## Page 6

Q1 A   mouth
B   gullet
C   stomach
D   small intestine
E   large intestine
F   rectum
G   anus

Q2 a) Starch molecules are large.
b) The starch molecules will have to be broken down into small molecules before they can get through the tubing.

Q3

Mouth   ○—■—△—○—○—▢—■—△—△—○

Stomach   ○—■—△—○—○   ▢—■—△—○
(or could be 3 or 4 sections)

Small intestine   ○  ■ △  ○  ■   △  ○
                      ■   ○   ▢      △

## Page 7

Q1 a) Glucose is present if the sample turns brick red when heated with Benedict's reagent.
b) No
c) The glucose came from inside the visking tubing bag.
d) The enzyme broke down the large starch molecules into small glucose molecules.
e) The tubing represents the small intestine.
f) The water represents the blood.

## Page 8

Q1 Food is digested by enzymes in the gut to form smaller molecules which can be absorbed into the blood.

Q2 a) A    stomach
B    small intestine
b) Conditions in the stomach are acidic.
c) Conditions in the small intestine are alkaline.

Q3      37 °C

Q4 a) i) Stomach enzymes need acidic conditions
ii) Small intestine enzymes need alkaline conditions.
b) These variables had to be kept constant to make it a fair test.
c) 37 °C is human body temperature so he knew that the enzymes would work at that temperature.
d) A water bath.

## Page 9

Q1 Blood

Q2 It passes out of our bodies in faeces.

Q3 It will be digested and the products will be absorbed and used in the cow's body.

Q4

## Unit 8B — Respiration

## Page 10

Q1 A, C, E

Q2 True

Q3 a) glucose
b) energy, high-energy drinks
c) blood, muscle cells

Q4 oxygen, glucose

Q5 a) safety glasses
b) oxygen
c) glucose
d) cells
e) controlled

## Page 11

Q1 a) 17°C
b) 19°C
c) heat energy

Q2 carbon dioxide, water

Q3 a) carbon dioxide produced by the yeast respiring
b) no

Q4 oxygen, water

# The Answers

## Page 12

Q1 glucose, bloodstream, cells, oxygen, transported, water

Q2

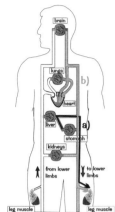

Q3 a) True
b) False
c) True
d) False
e) True

## Page 13

Q1 B

Q2

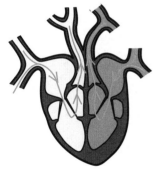

Q3 True

Q4 a) Theories based on experiment and observation are more scientific. They have evidence to back them up. Theories based on persuausive argument and imagination are unreliable because they argue things without solid evidence.
b) True
c) student's own answers

## Page 14

Q1 False

Q2 oxygen, glucose, respiration, energy, bloodstream

Q3 A, D, F

Q4 a) because it requires oxygen
b) They need to respire more to create the energy for exercise. Therefore they need to breathe in more oxygen.

Q5 a) oxygen
b) oxygen
c) energy

Q6 Answers might include: mountaineering at high altitudes, lung disease, strenuous exercise

## Page 15

Q1

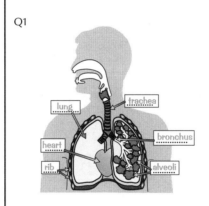

Q2 False

Q3 a) respiration

c) & b)

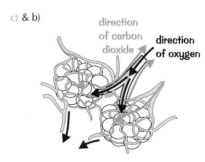

direction of carbon dioxide

direction of oxygen

d) It's a waste product of respiration.
e) So as much gas can be exchanged between the blood and alveoli as possible.

Q4 large surface area, very thin walls

Q5 It would be reduced.

## Page 16

Q1

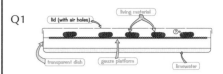

Q2 a) To make sure the change to the lime water was being caused by the living material.

b) Doing the experiment several times makes it easier to spot anomalous (randomly incorrect) results. They could average the results they got for each type of living material.

c) F

Q3 turned cloudy, respiring, more active, respiring more, stayed clear, plants

## Unit 8C — Microbes and Disease

## Page 17

Q1 Micro-organisms are so small that we can only see them when we use a microscope.

Q2 Viruses, bacteria and fungi are types of micro-organisms.
Viruses are much smaller than bacteria.
Mushrooms, toadstools and yeast are all fungi.
Many micro-organisms are useful.

Q3 A Fungi
B Bacteria
C Viruses

Q4

88

# *The Answers*

## *Page 18*

Q1  Respiration

Q2  Carbon dioxide

Q3  a)  Dough
    b)  Yeast
    c)  Carbon dioxide
    d)  Sugar is food for the yeast.

Q4  a)  A and C or B and D
    b)  A and B or C and D
    c)  To make it a fair test.

Q5  a)

b)  As the mass of sugar increases so does the height of dough.
    **OR**  When the mass of sugar doubles, the height of dough doubles.
    **OR**  The height of dough is directly proportional to the mass of sugar.
c)  As the mass of sugar increases so does the amount of carbon dioxide.
    **OR**  When the mass of sugar doubles, the amount of carbon dioxide doubles.
    **OR**  The amount of carbon dioxide is directly proportional to the mass of sugar.
d)  As the mass of sugar increases so does the rate of respiration.
    **OR**  When the mass of sugar doubles, the rate of respiration doubles.
    **OR**  The rate of respiration is directly proportional to the mass of sugar.
e)  Three sets of similar results helped the student to conclude that they were ii) reliable.

## *Page 19*

Q1  To grow bacteria in the laboratory they must be given **food**, **water** and **warmth**. Many grow well on the surface of a jelly-like material called **agar**. Various food substances can be added to the jelly to make **nutrient** agar. The agar is sterilised and put into a shallow **petri dish**. Bacteria are **streaked** across the surface of the solid agar using a **sterilised** wire **loop**.

Q2  a)  Never eat anything in a science laboratory.
    b)  Always wash your hands after working with bacteria.
    c)  After streaking agar stick adhesive tape around the petri dish.

Q3  Yoghurt — Bacteria
    Quorn(mycoprotein) — Fungi
    Antibiotic — Fungi
    Cheese — Bacteria
    Vinegar — Bacteria
    Alcohol — Yeast

Q4  **C** Bacteria produce acid and make the milk go sour. **E** The milk curdles and goes lumpy. **B** The solid part of the curdled milk is separated from the liquid part(whey). **A** Salt is added to the curds.
    **D** Bacteria are allowed to ripen the cheese, softening it and giving it its characteristic smell and flavour.

## *Page 20*

Q1  • Infectious diseases are caused by organisms that can be passed on to other animals.
    • Non-infectious diseases can not be caught because they are not caused by organisms.
    • Pathogens are organisms that cause disease.

Q2  influenza
    tuberculosis
    polio

Q3

| Infectious disease | Caused by |
|---|---|
| Rabies | |
| Common cold | |
| Tuberculosis | |
| Tetanus | |
| Food poisoning | |
| Whooping cough | |
| Athlete's foot | |
| Malaria | |

Q4  a)  Avoid crowded places.
    b)  Wash your hands after using the toilet.
    c)  Never leave food uncovered.

Q5  **Spread by droplets in air:**
    Rubella(German measles)
    Whooping cough
    Tuberculosis
    Common cold
    **Spread by contact with objects or infected people:**
    Chicken pox
    Whooping cough
    Athlete's foot
    Tuberculosis
    Impetigo
    **Spread in food and water:**
    Typhoid
    Dysentery
    Cholera
    Food poisoning
    **Spread by insect and animal vectors:**
    Malaria
    Sleeping sickness
    **Passed across the placenta:**
    Rubella (German measles)

*The Answers*

# *The Answers*

## *Page 21*

Q1  a)  Microbes cause food to rot.
 b)  Bacteria and Viruses
 c)  Air, food, touch, water, and
 animals.
 d)  The toxins.

Q2  Antibiotics, Disinfectants, antiseptics,
 strong, cells.

Q3  a)  Bacteria
 b)  Drinking water or eating food
 contaminated with human sewage.
 c)  The water pumps must have been
 infected with human sewage.  All
 the people receiving the water,
 would be at risk of Cholera.
 d)  Developing countries where they
 have no sewage system or
 treatment.

Q4  answers could include:
 Wash hand before handling food / after
 going to the toilet, to remove germs.
 Wash / bath regularly to remove
 microbes from your body.
 Clean teeth twice a day to remove
 bacteria that cause tooth decay.
 Cook food properly to kill harmful
 microbes.
 Cover food to prevent contamination.
 Boil water that has a contamination risk
 before you drink it.

Q5  a)  To stop the harmful microbes
 being spread.
 b)  Bacteria are living cells, viruses are
 not cells and only appear living
 when they have infected a host
 cell.
 c)  If sewage and waste water are
 treated before release they are no
 longer a breeding ground for
 harmful microbes.
 d)  Heating a food stuff (milk) to kill
 the microbes it contains.

## *Page 22*

Q1  • Tears are antiseptic to kill microbes
 • Scabs form a barrier to stop germs from
 getting into the blood.
 • Skin forms a barrier to germs and has
 glands that produce an antiseptic oil (to
 kill germs and keep it supple).
 • Lungs produce mucus to trap microbes
 and dust. Tiny hairs push mucus up to
 be swallowed
 • Stomach contains
 acid to kill microbes.

Q2  Correct order: **C**, **A**, **D**, **B**.

Q3  a)  Different micro-organisms that
 cause disease need different types
 of antibodies to attack them. **True**
 b)  White blood cells, called
 phagocytes, engulf invading
 microbes and digest them. **True**.
 c)  **False**, correction: People do not
 always get ill when exposed to
 potentially dangerous micro-
 organisms.
 d)  Antibodies produced by white
 blood cells can also neutralise
 poisons. **True**.

Q4  a)  Microscope.
 b)  Invade cells, reproduce, invade
 more cells and produce toxins.
 c)  To neutralise toxins made by
 invading microbes.

## *Page 23*

Q1  a)  Dettol, Domestos, TCP, Blue Fairy,
 and any other anti-microbial
 products.
 b)  Agar jelly.
 c)  To infect with a microbe.
 d)  Disinfectants are anti microbial, so
 stop the bacteria growing.

Q2  a)  penicillin
 b)  treatment
 c)  Not all
 d)  an accident.

Q3  bacteria, antibiotics, chemicals, kills.

Q4  a)  Alexander Fleming.
 b)  First to use penicillin.
 c)  Some are resistant.
 d)  To reduce the risk of bacteria
 developing resistance.
 e)  Not caused by bacteria.

## *Page 24*

Q1  injection, bacteria, immunised, kill,
 immunisation.

Q2  antibodies, placenta, breast milk,
 vaccines, immunity, quickly.

Q3  a)  By introducing childhood
 immunisation against many
 diseases.
 b)  True.
 c)  Mumps, measles and rubella
 vaccine.

Q4  a)  Viruses can cause diseases. **True**.
 b)  **False**, correction: Microbes can
 infect open wounds.
 c)  **False**, correction: Lister was the first
 surgeon to use antiseptics in
 operations.
 d)  **False**, correction: Microbes spread
 quickly in overcrowded conditions.
 e)  Your white blood cells help to
 protect you from disease. **True**.
 f)  Penicillin stops bacteria from
 reproducing. **True**.
 g)  **False**, correction: Once you have
 had measles you are immune and
 cannot catch it again.
 h)  **False**, correction: Platelets in your
 blood help to form scabs when you
 cut yourself.
 i)  Bacteria can sometime be useful
 rather than cause disease. **True**.

# The Answers

## Unit 8D — Ecological Relationships

### Page 25

Q1 a) The place where a plant or animal lives.
b) Frog — pond
Crab — sea
Deer — forest
Beetle - rotting tree stump
c) light, nutrients, water and space.
d) Plants photosynthesise and make their own food.

Q2 Animals with backbones are called **vertebrates**. There are five smaller groups of animals with backbones. These are birds, **mammals**, fish, **amphibians** and reptiles. Animals without backbones are called **invertebrates**. These can be sub divided into cnidarians, **flatworms**, roundworms, **segmented worms**, echinoderms, **molluscs** and **arthropods**. Arthropods are a group that have jointed **legs**.

Q3 **FISH** live in water and have gills. They are cold-blooded.
**MAMMALS** have hair, give birth to live young and feed them on milk. They are warm-blooded.
**REPTILES** have a dry, scaly, waterproof skin. They are cold-blooded and lay eggs on land.
**AMPHIBIANS'** young live in water as tadpoles and have gills. Adults live on land and have lungs.
**BIRDS** are covered in feathers, lay eggs and are warm-blooded.

Q4 a) Mosses \ liverworts.
b) Ferns.
c) Conifers.

### Page 26

Q1 a) Pitfall traps.
b) Dipping nets.
c) Kick samples.
d) Pooters.
e) Quadrats.
f) Tree beating.

Q2 a) Aquatic habitat - A water habitat, Terrestrial habitat - Land habitat.
b) **Aquatic habitat** - dissolved oxygen, temperature, pH.
**Terrestrial habitat** - light intensity, rainfall, temperature, soil pH, and humidity.
c) Different habitats have different environmental conditions.
d) To check for pollution.
e) Populations change with the seasons.
f) Taking many samples is more reliable than only taking one sample and populations may vary around the field.

Q3 a)

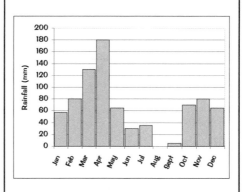

b) Very low (a drought).
c) Populations would fall because water is a basic survival need.

### Page 27

Q1 a) Grass, centipede, beetle, grasshopper — **meadow**
b) Hedgehog, oak trees, vole, owl. — **woodland**
c) Mussels, algae, flatfish, starfish. — **rock pool**

Q2 A — ladybird
B — earthworm
C — snail
D — beetle
E — millipede

Q3 a. Pond - dipping net.
Oak tree - tree beating.
b. The habitat provides different conditions and resources.
c. Pie Chart. (or bar chart)

### Page 28

Q1 Flowmeter: speed of a stream
Oxygen probe: dissolved oxygen
Light sensor: intensity of the sunlight
Temperature Probe: temperature
pH probe: acidity of river water

Q2 Temperature probe and datalogger connected to a p.c. set to record the temperature at suitable intervals.

Q3 warmed, daytime, plants, block, oxygen, different, colder, fewer, increased.

Q4 a) Arctic tundra - temperature
Desert - water
Rock pool - salinity
River - flow rate.
b) It can survive well in that area.
c) Thick fur, big feet to walk on snow, large volume to surface area to conserve heat, camouflaged.
d) Gives them a better chance of survival.

### Page 29

Q1 a) Group of organisms of the same species living in the same area at the same time.
b) Protection, mates, better to find food.
c) Quadrat.

Q2 water, nutrients, light, resources, nesting sites, burrow, predators.

Q3

| Limiting factor | In what way does it limit a population? (Give a reason) |
|---|---|
| Light | Limits plant populations - without light they cannot photosynthesize |
| Climate | Limits all populations - extreme temperatures can kill off organisms |
| Predators | Limits the number of prey - they get eaten |
| Shelter | Limits all populations - organisms need shelter to survive bad weather and to hide from predators |
| Space | Limits all populations - overcrowding spreads disease |
| Food | Limits all populations - food is an organism's energy source |
| Water | Limits all populations - all organisms need water to live |
| Oxygen | Limits all populations - all organisms respire, and hence need oxygen |
| Disease | Limits all populations - can kill off huge numbers in a population |

Q4 c), b), e), d), a).

# The Answers

## Page 30

Q1 a) algae → tadpole → stickleback → pike
b) algae.
c) tadpole.
d) stickleback.
e) stickleback and pike.
f) energy flow.
g) the sun.

Q2 a) food webs show all interconnections.
b) 6.
c) reduce or die off.
d) hawks drop in number, caterpillars increase in number and ladybirds increase in number.

Q3 a) A food chain put into bars to represent the number of organisms at each level.

b) i) & ii)

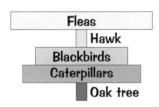

Q4 decomposers, nutrients, plants, growth.

## Unit 8E — Atoms and Elements

## Page 31

Q1 b, d, g, i and j

Q2 any sensible answer
eg wood, plastic, glass, rubber and steel

Q3 a, d, e, g, h

Q4 c, d, f, g, k

Q5 no

Q6 100

## Page 32

Q1 the first one

Q2 b)

Q3 b)   c)   d)

Q4 No.
There's more than one type of atom

Q5 a) iv
b) vi
c) ii
d) i
e) iii
f) v

## Page 33

Q1 Iron, copper, titanium and sodium

Q2 Most are non-magnetic

Q3 Oxygen and nitrogen

Q4 Textbooks, CD-roms, internet, encyclopaedia etc.

Q5 The metals are on the left-hand side

## Page 34

Q1 a, d, e and f are true
b, c and g are false

Q2

| Element | Symbol | State at 20°C | Metal/non-metal |
|---------|--------|---------------|-----------------|
| Cadmium | Cd | solid | metal |
| Potassium | K | solid | metal |
| Fluorine | F | gas | non-metal |
| Silicon | Si | solid | non-metal |

Q3 The non-metals are on the right

Q4 Mercury is a liquid at 20°C

Q5 Bromine is a liquid at 20°C

Q6 The gases are in the top right of the periodic table.

Q7 Iron, Cobalt, Nickel

## Page 35

Q1 a compound

Q2 molecule

Q3 a, b and d

Q4 a) hydrogen and oxygen
b) carbon and oxygen
c) sodium and iodine

Q5 a) A
b) B
c) one

Q6 a) methane
b) ammonia
c) carbon dioxide

## Page 36

Q1 a) a molecule of water
b) two atoms of hydrogen and one oxygen atom combine together to make a water molecule. Also accept answers which say that energy is given off, but it's the joining of atoms that we're after.
c) Gases
d) A liquid

Q2 a) solid – soft, silver-white, metallic
b) gas – dense and green
c) solid – salt: white grains

Q3 a) Hydrogen + oxygen = water
b) Iron + sulfur = iron sulfide
c) Sodium + iodine = sodium iodide
d) Silver + chlorine = silver chloride
e) Lithium + oxygen = lithium oxide
f) magnesium + oxygen = magnesium oxide

Q4 a)

b)

c)

d)

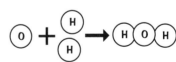

Q5 a) Hydrogen and oxygen
b) Electricity

# The Answers

## Page 37

Q1  a)  zinc oxide
    b)  zinc + oxygen → zinc oxide
    c)  Turn it to the yellow flame or turn it off.
    d)  Tongs
    e)  The top of the pale blue triangle.

Q2  The blue flame is hard to see, so you might not notice it, and end up burning yourself, your clothes or someone else.

Q3  a)  Bags under desks, or hung up on hooks.
    b)  Tied back.

Q4  a)  Copper and oxygen
    b)  Silver and chlorine
    c)  Carbon and oxygen
    d)  Chromium and oxygen
    e)  Sodium and fluorine
    f)  Iron and chlorine

Q5  a)  Sodium and chlorine
    b)  Iron and bromine
    c)  Magnesium and oxygen
    d)  Silver and bromine
    e)  Copper and oxygen
    f)  Calcium and chlorine

## Page 38

Q1  a)  impossible to tell
    b)  non-element
    c)  non-element
    d)  non-element
    e)  element
    f)  non-element

Q2  a)  element
    b)  element
    c)  non-element
    d)  element

Q3  a)  Substance X has increased in mass from 13g to 19g and it has changed from a shiny solid into a white powder.
    b)  Any sensible answer. Eg substance X reacted with something to form a new substance. It's being added to so it increases in weight and it's a new substance so its appearance changes.

Q4  a)  Sensible answers eg something escaped as a gas, it might have sublimated or it might have broken down into two different substances, eg calcium oxide and carbon dioxide.
    b)  You'd see if the remaining substance had the same reactions with acid as the original substance. You'd catch some of the escaping gas in a test tube, and test it to see if it was carbon dioxide.

## Unit 8F — Compunds and Mixtures

## Page 39

Q1  *A colourless gas*; made of two atoms of oxygen joined together; $O_2$

    *A white solid*; made of one atom of zinc joined to one atom of oxygen; **ZnO**

    *A colourless liquid*; two atoms of hydrogen joined to one atom of oxygen; $H_2O$

    *A colourless gas*; one atom of carbon joined to two atoms of oxygen; $CO_2$

    *A greenish gas that smells of swimming pools*; two atoms of chlorine joined together; $Cl_2$

Q2  a)  one
    b)  one
    c)  two
    d)  one
    e)  four
    f)  three

Q3  a)  one iron, two chlorine
    b)  one sodium, one bromine
    c)  one zinc, two chlorine
    d)  one magnesuim, one oxygen
    e)  one nitrogen, three hydrogen
    f)  one hydrogen, one nitrogen, three oxygen
    g)  one calcium, one carbon, three oxygen
    h)  two hydrogen, one sulfur, four oxygen
    i)  one aluminium, three chlorine
    j)  one nitrogen, four hydrogen, one chlorine
    k)  two iron, three oxygen
    l)  one potassium, one manganese, four oxygen

## Page 40

Q1  a)  A new compound has been formed
    b)  The sulfur and iron are joined together chemically/ the sulfur atoms are joined to the iron atoms
    c)  No

Q2  a)  No
    b)  All water molecules are identical

Q3  a)

## Page 41

Q1  a)  It melts into a sticky liquid and turns brown.
    b)  It still tastes sweet.
        Sensible reasons should be given for their answer eg Yes, because it tastes the same and its appearance is similar if you break it up. No because it has changed colour.
    c)  Any sensible answer. E.g. Yes because its colour change suggests that something has been added to it.

Q2  a)  Yes
    b)  Colour change, and a solid being formed

Q3  Change in colour; change in mass; gas being given off (bubbles in a liquid); solid being formed (liquid going from clear to cloudy)

Q4  Oxygen

Q5  a)  **Elements** are made of just one sort of atom.
    b)  The **atoms** in two different elements can join together in a chemical reaction
    c)  A molecule of a **compound** is made of different atoms joined together
    d)  You can tell what elements are in a compound by looking at the symbols in its **formula**.

# The Answers

## Page 42

Q1 a) and c) are compounds, b) and d) are mixtures

Q2 any sensible answers eg squash, tea, shampoo, soil, air

Q3 true

Q4 a) Heat it gently to evaporate off the water
b) chromatography (letting water spread out the ink over blotting paper)
c) Use a magnet to attract the iron filings

Q5 Nitrogen 78%; oxygen 21%; carbon dioxide 0.1% argon 0.9% (accept rounded up figures)

Q6 Sensible answers - these are suggestions: Liquid nitrogen is used for cooling. Nitrogen is used for making ammonia. Oxygen is used for bleaching, and is used instead of air in furnaces Animals need oxygen for respiration Plants need carbon dioxide for photosynthesis

Q7 The air you breathe out will have less oxygen and more carbon dioxide than the air you breathe in

Q8 No, because a mixture doesn't have a fixed composition. Also, mixture is pretty much the opposite of pure!

## Page 43

Q1 a) the melting point column
b) a gas
c) yes
d) yes
e) yes

Q2 They both mean the transition between solid and liquid, so they happen at the same temperature.

Q3 Nitrogen is only a liquid when it is between -210°C and -196°C.

Q4 No because it's a mixture and each gas in the mixture has its own boiling point.

Q5 a) Salt solution is a mixture
b) No. They don't

## Page 44

Q1 a) The stronger the solution, the lower the melting point
b) Mixtures don't have a fixed melting point. This is shown by the differing melting / freezing points.

Q2 Liquid A is a pure liquid

Q3 a) compound
b) element
c) compound, element
d) compound, element
e) compound, element
f) mixture
g) mixture

## Unit 8G — Rocks and Weathering

## Page 45

Q1 a), b), d)

Q2 a) The sandstone had absorbed some water. The change in mass was due to the mass of the water absorbed.
b) Air came out of little gaps in the rock as water went in.
c) Porous

Q3 Dull, grainy looking rock is more likely to let water pass through.

Q4 a — The one without gaps

## Page 46

Q1 The new statue is smoother. It's cleaner. Details are visible, and haven't been worn off. There are no cracks.

Q2 Plant roots (esp tree roots) can crack rock as they grow.

Q3 yellow-orange

Q4 a) time lapse photography - taking one photograph each day.
b) It's likely to be a mixture. The grains have different chemical properties.

## Page 47

Q1 a) It expands
b) expand: gets bigger
contract: gets smaller

Q2 a) It will freeze.
b) More pressure will be put on the cracks and they may get wider.
c) The diagrams should show the gaps widening and bits of rock splitting off from the the main bulk.

Q3 Conditions where the temperature often drops below freezing and rises again causing regular freezing and thawing of the water. (Wide changes in temperature cause rock to expand and contract, which also weakens it).

Q4 Scree is made of broken off bits of rock. It tells you that water had frozen and thawed in cracks in the rock lots of times, so weather conditions would have been frosty (with warmer days).

## Page 48

Q1 b, d, a, c

Q2 Where the water is moving slowly.

Q3 The smaller the particle the further it will be carried by the river.

Q4 a) Sensible experiment design involving different sized bits of stone flowing down a length of guttering or trough.
b) Any sensible answers relating to the experiment they have designed eg: size of sediment, speed of water, method of putting sediment in water, tilt of guttering, length of guttering, type of guttering etc.
c) They should list all variables except the size of sediment.
d) Answers should relate to thier experiment. Should include things like keeping the setup the same, measuring the distance carried in the same way, adding the sediment in the same way etc.

## Page 49

Q1 a) The corners get worn off
b) Why aye, man (or yes). The sediment would get bashed against the river bed, sides and other bits of sediment.

Q2 a) It's carrying lots of small sediment particles
b) Mud/sediment
c) Flood water

Q3 a) sediment
b) deposition

# The Answers

## Page 50

Q1  Sediment from the sea and rivers feeding the sea is deposited on the sea bed in layers.  Over millions of years these layers build up, putting the lower levels under so much pressure they form rock.

Q2  a)  Gravel — sediment with heavy grains settles faster.
    b)  sharp
    c)  blurry

Q3  a)  yes
    b)  More concentrated
    c)  Salt crusts and sediment

Q4  It'd be squashed, and become part of the rock - a fossil.

## Page 51

Q1  a)  The layers below are older
    b)  Similar ages

Q2  a)  iii
    b)  ii
    c)  i

Q3  Suitable paragraphs about fossil finding. Bonus points for citing sources.

## Unit 8H — The Rock Cycle

## Page 52

Q1  Particles of rock carried in moving water, and deposited.

Q2  any sensible answers eg limestone, sandstone, mudstone, marl

Q3  a) and c)

Q4  You'd see water and air bubbles coming out of the sand as it got squashed.

Q5  Any sensible answer.  eg
    Layers of sediment are deposited at the bottom of lakes, seas and oceans.  Lots of sediment is laid down over time. These layers of sediment are called strata.  The pressure at the bottom of deep layers of strata is very high.  The high pressure causes the grains of sediment to be squashed together tightly.  They are cemented together by other minerals and become rock.

Q6  a)  the water's squeezed out and it's glued together by other minerals
    b)  other minerals
    c)  water
    d)  fossils

## Page 53

Q1  No

Q2  a)  When the reaction is finished, no more carbon dioxide is given off
    b)  You'd grind up the rock into powder
    c)  You'd use the same mass of each, and grind them up the same.

Q3  a)  Portland stone (because of the seashells — smooth because it had been squashed a lot)
    b)  Oolithic limestone (because of the lumpy, ball-like structure)
    c)  a mixture.

## Page 54

Q1  a), d), e)

Q2  a)  Rock 2 is more porous
    b)  Rock 1 is harder

Q3  sensible answers, eg Slate is formed when shale is heated and placed under high pressure underground

Q4  The fossil would be deformed or destroyed.

Q5  The missing words are:
    sedimentary,  pressure, metamorphic, temperature, pressure

## Page 55

Q1  From below the Earth's crust (the Earth's mantle.

Q2  Ash, smoke, steam, volcanic bombs

Q3  Any sensible answers eg basalt, obsidian, pumice, granite

Q4  B

Q5  Crystals are formed by particles joining together in a regular pattern.  When magma cools slowly, the particles have more time to join together, so they can make bigger crystals.  (or similar answer)

## Page 56

Q1  Dense, shiny with crystals, or lighter, with bubbles in it.

Q2  Measure mass and volume of both.  Use displacement of water to measure the volume and scales to measure the mass. Divide mass by volume for each.  Ta-daaaah.

Q3  missing words:
    igneous, iron
    igneous, silica, dense
    igneous, silica
    a)  iron is heavier
    b)  more like gabbro

Q4  a)  light, porous and rough
    b)  Any sensible example eg Montserrat

Q5  a)  basalt
    b)  Any sensible example eg Hawaii

## Page 57

Q1  a) sedimentary
    b) metamorphic
    c) igneous

Q2  By the action of heat and high pressure

Q3  washed away and deposited deposits

Q4  a)  cooling quickly above the surface
    b)  cooling slowly below the surface
    c)  weathering
    d)  melting
    e)  metamorphism (from heat and pressure)
    f)  deposition of sediment

# The Answers

## Unit 81 — Heating and Cooling

### Page 58

Q1 Temperature is a measure of how hot something is.

Q2 Degrees Celsius (°C)

Q3 Below zero.

Q4 So that we know relatively, how hot something is

Q5
a) Icy pond — 0 °C or anything below zero
b) Outside in winter — around 2°C
c) Inside a classroom — about 20°C
d) Outside in summer — about 25 °C
e) Boiling water — 100 °C
f) Baker's oven — about 160°C
g) Body temperature — about 37°C

Q6
A — 1
B — 6
C — 3
D — 5
E — 2
F — 4

### Page 59

Q1 A), B) and F)

Q2 A = High temperature, B = heat flow, C = low temperature

Q3
a) All at room temperature.
b) A will be above room temperature, B & C at room temperature.
c) A, B and C will all be way above room temperature.

Q4
a) The temperature will increase.
b) The chemical energy in the fuel changes to heat and light energy. The heat energy warms the air up which rises by convection and heats the glass of the beaker. The flame itself is also in contact with the glass which heats up the water by conduction and then convection.
c) Chemical energy → heat and light energy
d) It would be higher.

### Page 60

Q1 Bicycle frame, end of stethoscope would be cold to the touch.

a) i) and ii) = outside temperature / 15°C
   iii) = 37 °C
b) In each case the fingers are warmer than the object so heat flows toward the object. Some objects feel cold as they conduct the heat away efficiently, the lunch box feels warm, as it is a poor conductor, so does not conduct the heat away well.
c) Conductors
d) Insulators

Q2 Insulators: b), c), f)
Conductors: a), d), e)

Q3 Conductors, metals, conductors, insulators

### Page 61

Q1
a) It was heated up by the Bunsen burner to 100°C.
b) Water is a poor conductor of heat energy — as a result the water could boil at the top but remains cold at the bottom.
c) The water would eventually conduct heat down and the ice would melt.

Q2
a) Solids
b) Solid
c) Yes, generally the closer the particles are together the better the substance is at conducting heat.

Q3
a) Team A
b) Team B
c) Heating one end of the solid and part of a liquid.
d) Heat energy is passed along the solid from particle to particle, hot particles move more and vibrate more so knock adjacent particle passing the movement along the solid. Shows how in a liquid particles are further apart and so pass heat around more slowly.
e) The team would not hold hands or link arms and slowly walk around in a random pattern. One of them could try and move round quickly and make all the others move quickly by bumping into them. This would not work as well as being in contact with each other as before.

### Page 62

Q1
gas    liquid    solid

Q2 The ball had expanded so does not fit in the hole

Q3
a) The oil expands and therefore takes up a larger volume, it therefore fills the space available in the capillary tube
b) The oil would move down the capillary tube.

Q4
a) Gas
b) More
c) As the air warmed, its particles moved further apart causing it to expand and move out of the capillary tube. The bubbles seen are the air escaping.
d) As the air cooled its particles began to move slower and get closer together, the gas therefore took up less volume and the red liquid moved up the capillary tube to fill this space.

Q5 Diagram should have particles (circles) with increased vibration (small gaps), but not in a liquid state as shown in Q1 above.

### Page 63

Q1 Second option is correct: Warm water is less dense than cold, so it rises causing a convection current.

Q2
a) The cold water is more dense than the warm water which will cause it to sink to the bottom of the bath.
b) Put a thermometer at top and then at bottom of water.
c) The hot and cold water have mixed due to convection and conduction between the two layers.

Q3 In both cases the cold (colourless) water goes to the bottom because it is more dense. The two layers can be clearly seen as the hot water on the top layer is coloured.

# The Answers

## Page 64

Q1 Convection, radiation, heat, medium, energy, vacuum

Q2 a) convection b) conduction c) radiation

Q3 Heat energy reaches Sarah by <u>radiation</u> and as warmed air in <u>convection</u> currents.

Q4 a) The black side
b) The black side
c) Diagram should have more or thicker arrows on the dark side of the metal plate

Q5 The silver/shiny teapot would keep a given volume of tea warmer as dark colour emits a greater amount of heat energy

Q6 Radioactive radiation is to do with the emission of radioactive material from the nucleus (centre of an atom), thermal radiation is simply the emission of heat energy (i.e. Infrared light).

## Page 65

Q1 Any from...double glazing, loft insulation, cavity wall insulation, curtains over windows, draft excluders.

Q2 Saves money spent on heating and saves heating resources and is more environmentally friendly.

Q3 The air-gap between double-glazed windows prevents heat loss by conduction as air is a poor conductor of heat. The air gap is also narrow to prevent heat loss by convection of the air.

Q4 a) The cavity stops heat loss caused by conduction.
b) Without the foam, heat would be transferred from the warm inner wall to the outer wall by convection of the air. Filling the cavity with foam traps the air in small pockets, preventing heat loss by convection.

Q5 Words should be changed to: **reflect**, **poor**, **conduction**, **insulating**.

## Page 66

Q1 a = melting, b= boiling, c = condensing (liquifying) d= freezing (solidifying).

Q2 a) Sodium.
b) 98 °C.
c) Possible answers: Boiling points are useful to know as they can be used to separate mixtures of substances by distillation, measuring the boiling of a substance can tell you about its purity, it is important to know how materials we use will change under different conditions.

Q3 a) The temperature increases.
b) The temperature remains constant.
c) The temperature increases.
d) The correct words are: temperature, weaken, particles, liquid.
e) Answer: The liquid salol would boil and turn into a gas.

Q4 D — gas cools, E — gas forms a liquid, F — liquid cools, G — solid forms from liquid, H — solid cools.

## Page 67

Q1 solid, liquid and gas.

Q2 melting, boiling, freezing, condensing (also accept solidifying, liquifying).

Q3 conduction, convection and radiation.

Q4 a) Below zero.
b) -113 °C.
c) -83 °C.

Q5

Warm air rising causes <u>convection</u> currents which create an onshore wind.

Ice cream is melted by <u>radiation</u> from the sun.

Sunbathers are warmed by <u>radiation</u> from the sun.

Waves cool the sand by <u>conduction</u>.

The air that lifts the balloon is heated by <u>convection</u>.

Sausages on barbeque grill are heated by <u>radiation</u> <u>conduction and convection</u>

The sausage burns Johnny by <u>conduction</u>

Q6 A blanket has small fibres which trap air between them. Air is a poor conductor of heat and so acts as an insulator, keeping you warm by reducing heat transfer. The loft insulation acts in the same way but the fibres are even smaller, trapping more air.

## Unit 8J — Magnets and Electromagnets

## Page 68

Q1 <u>Attracted by magnet</u>: nickel coin, iron nail, steel knife
<u>Not attracted by magnet</u>: Plastic cup, aluminium can, paper, lead soldier, wooden ruler, gold coin, polythene bag.

Q2 iron, steel, nickel
cobalt is the missing one

Q3 a) fridge door seal, holds notes
b) magnetic door catch
c) attracts steel screws
d) holds the can lid in position when removed
e) produces force on loudspeaker coil

Q4 a) A is a magnet
b) B is a magnet
c) C is not a magnet
d) Only two magnets can repel each other.

## Page 69

Q1 a) Paper is not magnetic.
b) The fridge door is not magnetic.
c) Magnetism does act through paper.

Q2 a) i) It will stay in place.
ii) It will stay in place.
iii) It will drop to the desk.
iv) It will stay in place.
v) It will drop to the desk.
vi) It will stay in place.

b) cardboard, aluminium, copper, tin
c) steel, iron
d) they are ferromagnetic (can be made into a magnet)

Q3 a) Stroking the iron nail in one direction with one pole of the bar magnet would magnetise the iron nail.
b) To see if it had become a magnet he could pour some iron filings on it — they will stick to one end if it is a magnet. (Any other non-magnetic steel or iron object could be used.)
c) Banging the nail vigorously or heating it strongly would destroy the nail's magnetism.

Q4 a) The second magnet is stronger.
b) Twice as strong.

# The Answers

## Page 70

Q1 a) It will settle with one end pointing towards the north pole.
b) a magnet
c) Between two small pointed supports at centre of compass needle.
d) A magnetic north pole (north seeking pole)
e) A magnetic south pole (south seeking pole)
f) i) south
 ii) north
 iii) south
 iv) south

Q2 a)

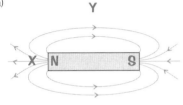

b) i) north     south
 ii) stronger
 iii) weaker
 iv) iron filings
 v) along

## Page 71

Q1 a)   b)

c)

Q2 a) i) Adjust the variable resistor.
 ii) Using the ammeter.
 iii) By observing how many small nails were picked up.
 iv) Increase the size of the current.
b) i) More nails would be picked up
 ii) Fewer nails would be picked up
 iii) Probably about the same number of nails would be picked up.

## Page 72

Q1 electric, temporary, attracts, opened, stops, away from, closed, starts.

Q2 a) It starts to flow
b) The current makes the core into an electromagnet which attracts the lever
c) The current starts to flow
d) Current in input circuit stops flowing, electromagnet stops being a magnet and no longer attracts lever, which moves back, the contacts in the output circuit open and current in the output circuit stops flowing

Q3 a)

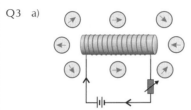

b) directions reversed
c) still point in same general direction as a), but will be influenced by earth's magnetic field
d) point N-S, in direction of earth's magnetic field.

## Unit 8K — Light

## Page 73

Q1 A   Star
 C   Laser
 F   Candle

Q2 C, D, B, A

Q3 Across a room -Almost instantly
 To the Moon -Just over a second
 From the Sun-Eight minutes
 From a star- Many years

Q4 a) false
b) true
c) false
d) true
e) true
f) false

## Page 74

Q1 a) reflect
b) opaque
c) absorb
d) transparent
e) translucent
f) reflect  absorb
g) transparent  transmit

Q2

| Transparent | Translucent | Opaque |
|---|---|---|
| glass | cloud | wood |
| water | fog | brick |
| Outer Space | tracing paper | lead |
| air | scratched glass | steel |

Q3 A   False
 B   False
 C   True
 D   False
 E   True
 F   True

Q4 a) Light travels in a straight line from the torch to the floor and gets absorbed.
b) Light reflects off the mirror and hits the bottom of the engine.
c) The light shining on the bottom of the engine goes back down to the mirror and then reflects up into the eyes of the mechanic.

# The Answers

## Page 75

Q1
a) Image
b) Inverted
c) Protractor
d) Incident ray
e) Periscope
f) Plane
g) Kaleidoscope
h) Normal
i) Reflected ray
j) Pepper's ghost

Q2 When light REFLECTS from a mirror you should measure all ANGLES with respect to the NORMAL. The angle that the light ray goes in at is called the angle of INCIDENCE. This is equal to the ANGLE of REFLECTION. The IMAGE in a mirror is INVERTED from side to side but not from top to bottom. This means that it is the right way up but the wrong way round.

Q3

Q4
a) A,H,I,M,O,T,U,V,W,X and Y (in some fonts!)
b) So that a driver can read it in the rear view mirror.
c) One mirror would make the image upsidedown. Two reflections will put the image the right way round again.

## Page 76

Q1
a) Refraction
b) Reflection
c) Refraction
d) Reflection
e) Refraction
f) Refraction (or cellulite!)
g) Refraction

Q2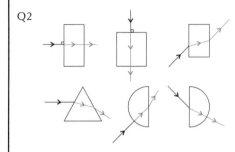

Q3
a) der = red
b) lube = blue
c) enger = green
d) I dingo = indigo
e) to vile = violet
f) go near = orange
g) yo well = yellow
h) ow Brian! = rainbow
i) simpr = prism
j) cures pmt = spectrum
k) so inspired = dispersion

Q4
a) Red, orange, yellow, green, blue, indigo and violet.
b) Indigo
c) White (hard to do in practice)
d) Infra red
e) Blue - lose 20 marks if you got that one wrong. (Joke.)
f) Violet
g) Red

## Page 77

Q1
a) True
b) True
c) False
d) True
e) False
f) False
g) True
h) False

Q2
a) If white light shines on a red filter GREEN and BLUE are absorbed but RED is transmitted.
b) If white light shines on a yellow surface BLUE is absorbed but RED and GREEN are reflected.
c) If blue light shines on a yellow filter NO light is transmitted.
d) If a coloured pencil reflects red and blue light then you would see the colour MAGENTA.
e) If yellow light shines on a green surface then GREEN is reflected.
f) If RED, GREEN and BLUE are absorbed completely then you see BLACK/NOTHING.

Q3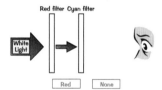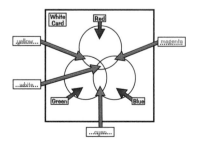

# The Answers

## Unit 8L — Sound

### Pages 78

Q1 a) vibrating
b) pitch, low
c) pitch, high
d) loud, volume
e) quiet, volume

Q2 a) Using a thicker string ... gives a lower note.
b) Tightening the string ... gives a higher note.
c) Making the string shorter ... gives a higher note.
d) Making a bigger vibration ... gives a louder note.

Q3 a) It is vibrating.
b) i) it gets louder.
ii) it stays the same.

### Pages 79

Q1 loudness, amplitude, vibration(s), pitch, frequency, vibrates

Q2 a) i) D
ii) A
iii) B
b) B and C

Q3 Guitar:
a) pluck the string
b) the string
c) puck the string harder
d) make string shorter or use a thinner string
Trombone:
a) blow it
b) the air in it
c) blow harder
d) make it shorter by pulling the slider back
Triangle:
a) hit it
b) the metal
c) hit it harder
d) you can't!
Violin:
a) bow the string, or pluck it
b) the string
c) bow it or pluck it harder
d) make string shorter or use a thinner string
Drum:
a) hit it
b) the drumskin
c) hit it harder!
d) make the skin tighter

## Page 80

Q1 a) light travels faster than sound
b) it travels as waves where the air particles vibrate backwards and forwards
c) 2 kilometres

Q2 a) the sound gets fainter and fainter until eventually you can't hear it
b) you would see the hammer hitting the gong
c) i) air (don't accept 'nothing')
ii) a vacuum (accept 'nothing')
d) the foam reduces the vibrations travelling through the legs of the clock to the jar base.
e) sound needs something, a 'medium', to travel through

Q3 180 m/s ($108 \div 0.6 = 180$ m/s)

Q4 a)

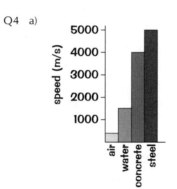

b) solids, gases
   liquids, gases

## Page 81

Q1 a) The voice vibrates the air, which in turn vibrates the cup. The voice travels along the string as vibrations and is amplified by the cup at the other end.
b) It has to be stretched or the vibrations wouldn't get passed along.
c) When the vibrations reach the corner they are stopped.
d) Do a test on how well someone can hear a quiet message along a string (eg what is quietest sound audible), then do same with a steel wire. For fair test must be same length of wire, and same tension ('force', 'amount of stretch'). Each sound used should be the same volume and pitch for both materials.

Q2 Account should include some of following points: particles (or 'atoms', 'molecules') in front of vibrating object move backwards and forwards, this makes next particles do same, and so on. Because particles in a solid are closer together and held in lattice they pass on vibrations faster than in liquids. Gases are the slowest.

Q3 a) i) bats, dolphins, dogs
ii) elephants
b) ultrasound (or ultrasonic)
c) to detect insects or find their way around at night (accept 'echo-location' or 'sonar', do **not** accept 'radar')

# *The Answers*

## *Page 82*

Q1 a)   1 = pinna
Collects sound and funnels them down the ear canal.
2 = eardrum
Vibrates when sound hits it.
3 = three ear bones
Passes the sound along the middle ear.
4 = cochlea
Translates sound into electrical signals.
5 = (auditory) nerve
Sends electrical signals to brain.

b)   object vibrates, air vibrates, eardrum vibrates, ear bones vibrate, hairs vibrate in cochlea and produce electrical signals, nerve carries electrical signals to brain

Q2 a)   i) produce electrical signals (or oscillations/vibrations)
ii) to vibrate and produce sound
iii) to measure pitch/frequency of sound

b)   volume/amplitude, distance from speaker, as little background sound as possible

Q3 a)   help it detect danger quickly

b)   Use a suitable source of sound, test someone to find loudness of sound they can just detect with and without cardboard 'ears'. Fair test if same sound source used (eg same frequency if speaker) and as little background sound as possible. Better to repeat several times for each test to improve reliability.

## *Page 83*

Q1 a)   decibel

b)   Exposure to loud sounds can damage hearing eg tinnitus, temporary deafness. Ear defenders cut down loudness (or 'intensity' of sound energy) in the ear.

Q2 a)   use same string, same tension

b)   i) hertz
ii)

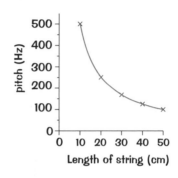

c)   i) 336 Hz
ii) 25 cm
(nb for i) and ii) check 'correct' answer read from pupil's graph)

d)   ...lower the pitch.
...frequency, is doubled.

Q3 a)   an echo

b)   i) 1½ seconds
ii) 1½ seconds
iii) 2250 metres

## *Page 84*

Q1 a)   Equipment should be arranged in a suitable way which would work. Insulation should surround the speaker. Microphone should be positioned to record the sound at a measured distance and should be connected up to the loudness meter.

b)   thickness of insulation, loudness of sound both without and with the insulation.

c)   Distance between sound source and loudness meter must be same with and without insulation. Should use same frequency of sound and have as little background sound as possible.

Q2 a)   i) vacuum
ii) eardrum
iii) speed
iv) insulation
v) tinnitus
vi) vibrate
vii) frequency
viii) loudness
ix) decibel

secret word = "amplitude".